# REVISION BOOK IN ORDINARY LEVEL PHYSICS

*by*

## M. NELKON

M.Sc., F.Inst.P., A.K.C.
*Formerly Head of the Science Department, William Ellis School, London*

**THIRD EDITION**

## Heinemann Educational Books
LONDON

Heinemann Educational Books Ltd
LONDON EDINBURGH MELBOURNE AUCKLAND TORONTO
HONG KONG SINGAPORE KUALA LUMPUR NEW DELHI
IBADAN NAIROBI LUSAKA JOHANNESBURG
KINGSTON

ISBN 0 435 67661 X

© M. Nelkon 1968, 1970, 1973

First published 1968
Second edition 1970
Third edition 1973
Reprinted 1975, 1976

Published by Heinemann Educational Books Ltd
48 Charles Street, London W1X 8AH
Text set in 10/11 pt. Monotype Times New Roman, printed by
letterpress, and bound in Great Britain at The Pitman Press, Bath

# Preface

This book is designed to help Ordinary-level students with the modernised Physics syllabus of Examining Boards, which now includes sections on molecules and matter, waves, electron physics and radioactivity. It does not replace any textbooks of Physics but supplements them, and as it contains Notes the text is necessarily concise. In it the principal points in the subject have been compared and contrasted, and there are numerical examples in illustration of the topics. It is hoped that it will be particularly useful for revision purposes prior to Ordinary-level examinations in Physics, Physics-with-Chemistry and General Science.

## Third Edition

In this edition some notes on Gravitation and Planetary Motion have been added. The text has been revised further in SI units, with more use of the 'newton' and the 'kilogramme' in calculations. In addition to the use of the 'joule' in Heat, recommended names such as 'specific heat capacity', 'specific latent heat' and 'linear expansivity' have been adopted.

## 1975 Reprint

In this reprint the newton has now been used in the section on 'Forces due to Fluids' and some misprints have been corrected. I am grateful to correspondents for their helpful comments on various points.

# To the Student

The following hints will be found useful in answering examination questions:

1. *Descriptive Questions*, e.g. 'describe the moving-coil ammeter'.
   (*a*) Draw a neat diagram with ruler and pencil.
   (*b*) *Either* label the diagram with letters A, B, C, etc., and use the letters in your description, *or* write the names of the main parts of the apparatus on your diagram.

2. *Experiments*, e.g. 'describe how the resistance of a lamp filament is measured.'

   (*a*) Draw a neat labelled diagram with ruler and pencil.
   (*b*) Write out the experiment under these headings:
      (*i*) Apparatus used—refer to the diagram.
      (*ii*) Method (or Account)—describe the experiment step by step, stating the readings or observations taken and any special precautions to obtain an accurate result.
      (*iii*) Calculation—take imaginary but reasonable values, *or* use symbols, and show how the result is calculated.
      (*iv*) Conclusion—state the conclusion of the experiment if it is one to verify a particular law, or state the result if a calculation has been done and give the units.

3. *Problems*. There is an appropriate formula to every problem, e.g. in questions with uniform acceleration the formula required may be $v = u + at$ or $v^2 = u^2 + 2as$. Even if the whole question cannot be done, write down the appropriate formula or formulae, and substitute the numerical values of the quantities given in the question. Be particularly careful to consider the *units* of the quantities before substituting.

# Contents

## ACKNOWLEDGEMENT

*Much of the modern physics sections in this book, such as Sections 2, 4, 10, 11, 12, are based on material from the author's* Principles of Physics *published by Chatto & Windus, Ltd.*

# 1 Mechanics

## DYNAMICS

### Definitions

1. *Speed* = distance travelled per unit time (Fig. 1 (*a*)). It is a *scalar* quantity—it has magnitude only. Units: 'm/s' or 'km/h'. Note that

$$36 \text{ km/h} = 10 \text{ m/s}$$

2. *Velocity* = displacement per unit time *or* distance travelled in a constant direction per unit time *or* *displacement/time*. It is a *vector*

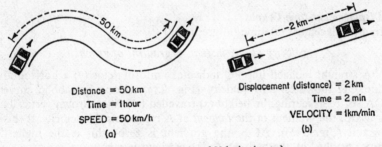

Distance = 50 km
Time = 1 hour
SPEED = 50 km/h
(a)

Displacement (distance) = 2 km
Time = 2 min
VELOCITY = 1 km/min
(b)

FIG. 1. Speed (*scalar*) and Velocity (*vector*)

quantity—it has both magnitude and direction, whereas 'speed' has magnitude only (Fig. 1 (*b*)). A car moving round a circle at constant speed has a different velocity at each point, because the velocity is in the direction of the tangent to the circle at the particular point and this direction varies with the position of the car.

*Uniform velocity* is the velocity of an object which has equal displacements in equal times, no matter how small the times may be.

1

**3.** *Acceleration* = velocity change per unit time *or* rate of change of velocity *or velocity change/time.* It is a vector. Units: metre per second per second or m/s².

*Uniform acceleration* is the acceleration of an object whose velocity increases by equal amounts in equal times, no matter how small the times may be.

*Acceleration due to gravity, g,* is the acceleration due to the gravitational pull of the earth. It varies all over the world, being greatest at the poles and least at the equator owing to the shape of the earth. *g* may be taken as 9·8 m/s², or, in round figures, 10 m/s², a value used frequently.

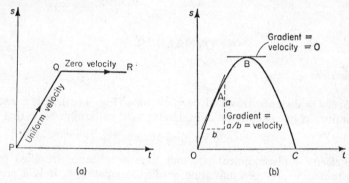

Fig. 2.    Distance–time Graphs

### Displacement-time Graphs

In a displacement (*s*)–time (*t*) graph,

*velocity at any instant = gradient of graph*

A straight inclined line PQ indicates uniform velocity; a horizontal line QR indicates zero velocity (Fig. 2 (*a*)). For a parabolic curve OABC, representing the height (*s*) travelled by a ball thrown vertically upward, the gradient of the *tangent* at A represents the velocity at this instant (Fig. 2 (*b*)). At B, the gradient is zero—this is the highest point reached by the ball. At A, the gradient is *a/b*.

### Displacement-time² Graph

When an object moves from rest with a uniform acceleration *a*, then $s = \frac{1}{2}at^2$. Thus a straight-line graph OA between *s* and *t²* (*not t*) passing through the origin O indicates a uniform acceleration, *a* (Fig. 3). Further,

$$\text{gradient of line} = \tfrac{1}{2}a \qquad \qquad \ldots(1)$$

so that *a* can be found after plotting *s* v. *t²*.

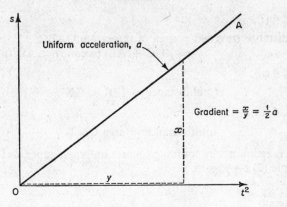

FIG. 3. Uniform acceleration

## Velocity (v)–time (t) Graphs

In these graphs, (i) *acceleration* = gradient at time concerned, (ii) *distance (displacement)* = area between graph and time-axis.

In Fig. 4 (*a*), the straight inclined line OA represents uniform (constant) acceleration of magnitude AD/OD; the horizontal line AB represents uniform velocity or zero acceleration; and the inclined line

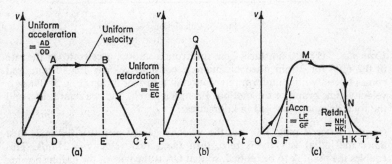

FIG. 4. Velocity–time graphs

BC represents uniform retardation of magnitude BE/EC. In Fig. 4 (*b*), a lift ascends with uniform acceleration = QX/PX, and then undergoes uniform retardation = QX/XR. In Fig. 4 (*c*), a train with variable acceleration has a magnitude at L = gradient of *tangent* to curve = LF/GF, and a retardation at N of magnitude NH/HK. If the vertical axis represents velocity in *m/s*, for example, and the horizontal axis represents time in *second*, then, from the numerical values on the scales,

acceleration is in 'metre per second² or m/s²'

In Fig. 4 (i),

total distance travelled = area of trapezium OABC
$$= \tfrac{1}{2}(OC + AB) \text{ (second)} \times AD \text{ (m/s)}$$

In Fig. 4 (ii),

$$\text{total distance} = \tfrac{1}{2}PR \times QX$$

In Fig. 4 (iii),

$$\text{total distance} = \text{area OMT}$$

The area is estimated by counting squares on graph paper, as illustrated in Example (2) on page 5.

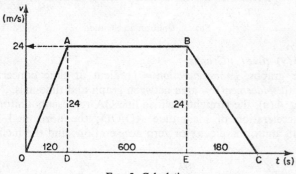

FIG. 5. Calculation

*Examples.* (1) A train starts from rest from a station, accelerates at the rate of 0·2 m/s² for 2 min, then maintains a constant velocity for 10 min, and comes to rest with a uniform retardation in a further 3 min (Fig. 5). Draw a velocity–time graph of the motion. From the graph, find the retardation and the total distance travelled in kilometres.

*Graph.* After 2 min, 120 sec, the velocity gained = 120 × 0·2 = 24 m/s. Since the initial velocity is zero, then the actual velocity = 24 m/s. This enables the point A to be plotted, so that OA is the part of the graph showing the uniform acceleration.

Now draw the line AB parallel to the time-axis so that AB or DE represents 10 min or 600 s. Finally, join B to C, which is 3 min or 180 s further than E on the time-axis.

*Calculations.* (1) Retardation along BC

$$= \frac{\text{velocity change}}{\text{time}} = \text{gradient of BC}$$

$$= \frac{BE}{EC} = \frac{24 \text{ m/s}}{180 \text{ s}}$$

$$= 0·13 \text{ m/s}^2$$

(2) Total distance
= area of trapezium OABC
= $\frac{1}{2}$(AB + OC) × AD
= $\frac{1}{2}$(600 + 900) × 24 m/s
= 18,000 m = 18 km

(2) The graph OAB in Fig. 6 is a velocity–time graph. Where is the acceleration (i) zero, (ii) a maximum? Estimate the maximum acceleration

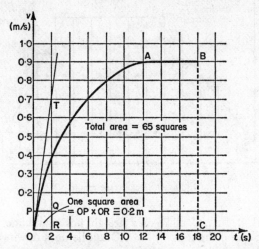

FIG. 6. Calculation

and the distance travelled in the time OC. What motion could be represented by the graph OAB?

(i) The acceleration is zero along AB as the velocity is constant here.

(ii) Maximum acceleration occurs at O. The acceleration is given by the gradient of the *tangent* OT at O to the curve. Thus

$$\text{acceleration} = \frac{RT}{OR} = \frac{0\cdot7 \text{ m/s}}{2 \text{ s}} = 0\cdot35 \text{ m/s}^2$$

Distance travelled in time OC = area OABC. Counting squares on the graph paper, there are about 65 squares. Now the square in the box OPQR represents a distance = OP (m/s) × OR (s) = $0\cdot1 \times 2 = 0\cdot2$ m.

∴ area OABC represents a distance = $65 \times 0\cdot2$ m = 13 m

Fig. 6 may represent the vertical velocity of an object released from a height which reaches a maximum (terminal) velocity. See p. 61.

*Ticker-timer and -tape*
With a ticker-timer, the distance moved by the tape between successive ticks (1/50 sec say) is proportional to the average velocity in this time-interval. Thus (i) *length* of paper in successive equal time-intervals

represents velocity, (ii) *width* of paper can represent equal times. Thus if the tops of the pasted strips A, . . ., B, all in five-tick lengths, lie on a straight inclined line, this shows the motion is one of *uniform acceleration* (Fig. 7).

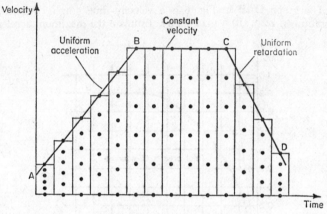

FIG. 7. Ticker-tape graph

If the tops, B, . . ., C, all lie on a straight horizontal line, the velocity is constant; and if the tops C, . . ., D, all lie on a downward straight line, this shows uniform retardation.

*Calculations.*   (1) If A and B represent parts of the tape of trolley run, calculate the average acceleration and the distance travelled from A to B (Fig. 8).

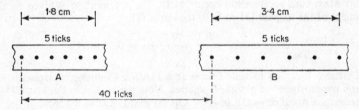

FIG. 8. Ticker-tape measurement

From A, time = 5 ticks = 5/50th s = 1/10th s; distance travelled = 1·8 cm. Thus velocity = 1·8/1/10 = 18 cm/s.

From B, time = 5 ticks = 5/50th s = 1/10th s,

$$\therefore \text{ velocity} = \frac{3\cdot4 \text{ cm}}{1/10 \text{ s}} = 34 \text{ cm/s}$$

$$\therefore \text{ average acceleration} = \frac{\text{velocity change}}{\text{time}}$$

$$= \frac{(34 - 18) \text{ cm/s}}{40/50 \text{ s}}$$

$$= 20 \text{ cm/s}^2 \qquad \ldots(\text{i})$$

Distance travelled = average velocity × time

$$= \frac{(18 + 34)}{2} \times \frac{40}{50} = 20 \cdot 8 \text{ cm}$$

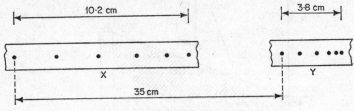

FIG. 9. Ticker-tape measurement

(2) If X and Y are parts of the tape of a run, estimate the average retardation for the distance between X and Y, which is 35 cm (Fig. 9).

$$\text{Average velocity at X} = \frac{10 \cdot 2 \text{ cm}}{5/50 \text{ s}} = 102 \text{ cm/s}$$

$$\text{Average velocity at Y} = \frac{3 \cdot 8 \text{ cm}}{5/50 \text{ s}} = 38 \text{ cm/s}$$

Thus along 35 cm, the average velocity $= \dfrac{102 + 38}{2} = 70$ cm/s

$$\therefore \text{ time taken} = \frac{35 \text{ cm}}{70 \text{ cm/s}} = \tfrac{1}{2} \text{ s}$$

$$\therefore \text{ average retardation} = \frac{\text{velocity change}}{\text{time}}$$

$$= \frac{102 - 38}{1/2} = 128 \text{ cm/s}^2$$

*Equations of Linear Motion*
If $u$ = initial velocity, $v$ = final velocity, $a$ = uniform acceleration, $t$ = time, $s$ = displacement (distance in constant direction), then

$$v = u + at, \quad s = ut + \tfrac{1}{2}at^2, \quad v^2 = u^2 + 2as$$

*Proofs.* 1. $v = u + at$: Since $a$ is the increase in velocity per second, then $a \times t$ is the increase in velocity after $t$ sec. Now $u$ is the initial velocity.

$$\therefore \text{ final velocity, } v = u + at$$

2. $s = ut + \frac{1}{2}at^2$:

Displacement, $s$ = average velocity × time

$$= \left(\frac{u + v}{2}\right) \times t$$

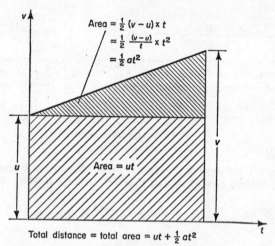

Total distance = total area = $ut + \frac{1}{2}at^2$

Fig. 10. Distance formula

But $v = u + at$,

$$\therefore s = \frac{u + u + at}{2} \times t = ut + \frac{1}{2}at^2$$

The '$\frac{1}{2}$' arises because the average velocity with uniform (constant) acceleration is half the sum of the initial and final velocities.

Fig. 10 shows how the formula for $s$ can be found using the velocity-time graph.

3. $v^2 = u^2 + 2as$:

Displacement, $s$ = average velocity × time

$$= \frac{u + v}{2} \times \frac{v - u}{a}$$

since $v = u + at$. Simplifying, we have:

$$v^2 - u^2 = 2as \quad \text{or} \quad v^2 = u^2 + 2as$$

In applying the formulae, note that:

(1) A retardation or deceleration is a negative acceleration, so that $a$ is negative on substitution.

(2) In a mixture of units, such as velocity in km/h, distance in cm and time in seconds, *all the quantities must be brought to the same units.* For example, change km/h to m/s and cm to m in the calculation concerned.

(3) In problems, first change all the quantities to common units and then write down the values of $v$, $u$, $a$, $t$ or $s$ which may be given. Now write down the three equations of linear motion ($v = u + at$, $s = ut + \frac{1}{2}at^2$, $v^2 = u^2 + 2as$) and choose the equation which would have only *one* unknown when your values are substituted in it.

*Example.* A car travelling at 72 km/h undergoes a uniform retardation of 50 cm per s$^2$. Find (i) the time for the velocity to decrease to one-quarter of its value, (ii) the distance travelled in this time.

$$72 \text{ km/h} = \frac{72 \times 1000 \text{ m}}{3600 \text{ s}} = 20 \text{ m/s} = u.$$

Final velocity $= \frac{1}{4} \times 72$ or 18 km/h $= 5$ m/s $= v$

(i) Using $v = u + at$, and $a = -50$ cm/s$^2$ $= -0\cdot5$ m/s$^2$,

$$\therefore 5 = 20 - 0\cdot5t$$

$$\therefore t = \frac{15}{0\cdot5} = 30 \text{ s}$$

(ii) Using $v^2 = u^2 + 2as$,

$$\therefore 5^2 = 20^2 - 2 \times 0\cdot5 \times s$$

$$\therefore s = \frac{20^2 - 5^2}{1} = 375 \text{ m}$$

## Determination of g

(1) *Free-fall.* Acceleration due to gravity, $g$, can be measured by a *free-fall* method, using a centisecond clock (one reading to hundredths second), an electromagnet with an attracted steel ball-bearing B, and a metal flap P vertically below B (Fig. 11 (*a*)). The height $h$ of B above P can be varied. When B is released from the electromagnet the clock starts automatically. It stops as soon as B strikes P, which then breaks a contact with the clock.

*Calculation.* $h = \frac{1}{2}gt^2$, or $g = 2h/t^2$. A graph of $h$ (varying from 0·8 to 1·4 m for example) is plotted against $t^2$, starting from the zero. The points lie on a straight line OA, showing the acceleration is *uniform* (see p. 6) (Fig. 11 (*b*)). The gradient, AX/XO, is then measured from the line. From $g = 2h/t^2$, $g$ is twice the gradient and is calculated.

(2) *Pendulum Method.* The period, $T$, the time for one complete to-and-fro oscillation, $= 2\pi\sqrt{(l/g)}$, where $l$ is the length of the pendulum (Fig. 12 (*a*)). In the experiment to determine $g$ by oscillations, (i) time a large number of oscillations, e.g. 30, (ii) have a small swing, (iii) use

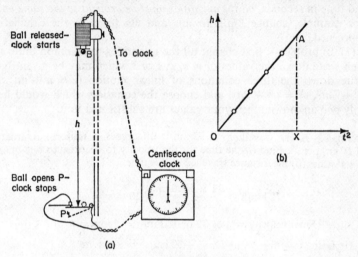

FIG. 11. Free-fall measurement of $g$

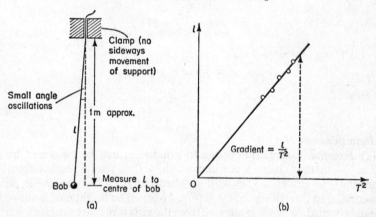

FIG. 12. Pendulum measurement of $g$

a long thread such as 1 metre, (iv) measure $l$ from the point of suspension to the centre of the bob used.

Since $g = 4\pi^2 l/T^2$, five different lengths of $l$ can be taken and $T$ measured each time. A graph of $l$ v. $T^2$ is a straight line passing through the origin (Fig. 12 (*b*)). The gradient $= l/T^2$, and hence $g = 4\pi^2 \times$ gradient.

## Motion under Gravity

Acceleration due to gravity, $g$, acts vertically downwards, and $g = 9.8$ m/s$^2$, approx. To simplify arithmetic, $g$ may be taken roughly as 10 m/s$^2$.

A falling object thus has roughly an acceleration of 10 m/s$^2$. A ball thrown vertically upwards has a *retardation* of roughly 10 m/s$^2$. In the latter case, we substitute $a = -10$ m/s$^2$ in equations of motion such as $v = u + at$, $s = ut + \frac{1}{2}at^2$, $v^2 = u^2 + 2as$.

*Example.* **1.** A heavy ball is dropped from a height of 20 metres. Find (i) the velocity just before striking the ground, (ii) the time to reach the ground. (Assume $g = 10$ m/s$^2$.)

(i) We have $s = 20$ m, $u =$ initial velocity $= 0$, $a = 10$ m/s$^2$. From $v^2 = u^2 + 2as$,

$$\therefore v^2 = 2 \times 10 \times 20 = 400$$

$$\therefore v = 20 \text{ m/s}$$

(ii) From $s = ut + \frac{1}{2}at^2$,

$$20 = \frac{1}{2} \times 10 \times t^2$$

$$\therefore t^2 = 4 \quad \text{or} \quad t = 2 \text{ s}$$

**2.** A ball is thrown vertically upwards with an initial velocity of 54 km/h. Assuming $g = 10$ m/s$^2$, calculate (i) the time to reach the greatest height, (ii) the magnitude of this height, (iii) the time to return to the thrower.

Initial velocity, $u = 54$ km/h $= 15$ m/s
The acceleration, $a = -10$ m/s$^2$, and final velocity, $v = 0$.

(i) From $v = u + at$,

$$\therefore 0 = 15 - 10t \quad \text{or} \quad t = 1.5 \text{ s}$$

(ii) From $v^2 = u^2 + 2as$,

$$\therefore 0 = 15^2 - 2 \times 10 \times s$$

$$\therefore s = 11\frac{1}{4} \text{ m}$$

(iii) Time to return to thrower $= 2 \times$ time to reach greatest height
$$= 3 \text{ s}$$

## Vectors: Adding by Parallelogram and Triangle Method

Speeds of 30 km/h and 40 km/h added together $= 70$ km/h. Speeds can always be added together arithmetically because they are *scalars* (p. 1).

*Velocities* of 30 km/h and 40 km/h can be added together only when their direction as well as magnitude are taken into account. Velocities (like displacements) are *vectors* (p. 1). They are hence added by a vector method.

(1) *Parallelogram Method.* Represent the two velocities by two lines OA, OB to scale from a point O (Fig. 13). Draw the parallelogram OACB. The diagonal OC then represents the sum or *resultant velocity* both in magnitude and direction, on the same scale as OA and OB.

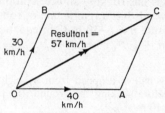

FIG. 13. Parallelogram method for resultant

Note carefully that the length of the resultant OC and its direction depend *considerably* on the angle BOA between the directions of the two velocities.

(2) *Triangle Method.* Represent one velocity (40 km/h) by a line OA to scale (Fig. 14). From A draw a line AB to represent the second

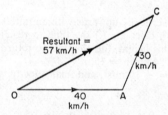

FIG. 14. Triangle method for resultant

velocity (30 km/h) completely. (Note that the two arrows on the lines OA, AB follow each other.) Then OB represents the resultant velocity of OA and AB. Either the parallelogram *or* the triangle method can be used for adding velocities or any other vectors such as forces (p. 36).

### Subtraction of Velocities

*Relative Velocity.* Suppose two trains, A and B, are travelling in the same direction on parallel lines with velocities of 70 and 50 km p h. The velocity of A relative to B = $\vec{v_A} - \vec{v_B}$ = 70 − 50 = 20 km p h, in the direction concerned (Fig. 15 (a)). (Arrows above $v_A$ and $v_B$ indicate vector quantities, that is, quantities which have direction.)

If two velocities C and D are not in the same direction, the *velocity of C relative to* D = $\vec{v_C} - \vec{v_D} = \vec{v_C} + (-\vec{v_D})$ (Fig. 15 (b)). The velocity

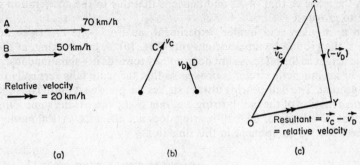

Fig. 15. Relative velocity

$-\overrightarrow{v_D}$ is represented by a line equal in magnitude to the velocity D but drawn in the opposite direction. Thus OX represents $\overrightarrow{v_C}$, and XY represents $-\overrightarrow{v_D}$ (Fig. 15 (c)). Hence OY represents $\overrightarrow{v_C} + (-\overrightarrow{v_D})$ or $\overrightarrow{v_C} - \overrightarrow{v_D}$. It is therefore the relative velocity of C to D in magnitude and direction.

### Components

Two coins A and B, struck simultaneously on the edge of a table so that A shoots forward with a horizontal velocity $u$ while B drops straight down to the ground, are heard to reach the ground simultaneously, whatever the value of $u$.

*Conclusions.* (1) The vertical motion of B is independent of its horizontal motion or velocity $u$, and vice-versa. (2) The vertical motion of

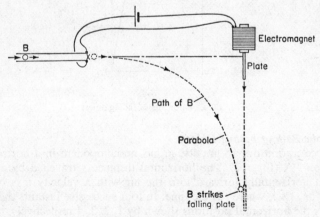

Fig. 16. Experiment on components of $g$

B is the same as that of A, and hence is that due to the acceleration $g$ due to gravity.

In a 'monkey and hunter' experiment, an iron plate is suspended above the ground by an electromagnet (Fig. 16). A ball-bearing, at the same height as the plate, is shot horizontally towards it—simultaneously, the electromagnetic circuit is broken so that the plate falls vertically to the ground. The ball-bearing always strikes the plate as it falls. Thus the *vertical* motion of the ball-bearing and that of the plate is the same—the horizontal velocity of the ball-bearing does not affect its vertical motion since it has no component in this direction.

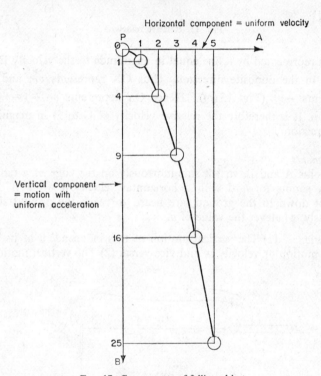

FIG. 17. Components of falling object

### Parabolic Path of Falling Object

The acceleration due to gravity, $g$, has no component in a horizontal direction PA (Fig. 17). The horizontal distance $s$ travelled by a ball thrown horizontally forward into the air with a velocity $u$ is hence $s = ut$ or $s \propto t$, where $t$ is the time. In four successive instants the ball reaches the horizontal positions shown by 1, 2, 3, 4 respectively.

The vertical distance PB travelled, $s = \frac{1}{2}gt^2$ in the same time $t$.

There is no initial velocity in a vertical direction, since $u$ is horizontal. Hence $s \propto t^2$ for the vertical distances. Thus in times 1, 2, 3, 4, 5 the vertical distances reached are proportional to $1^2, 2^2, 3^2, 4^2, 5^2$, or to 1, 4, 9, 16, 25. Fig. 17 shows the five positions of the ball, which all lie on a parabolic curve.

### Acceleration Down Inclined Plane

An object moving freely down a smooth inclined plane at an angle $\theta$ to the horizontal (Fig. 18) has an acceleration due to gravity of

$$g \sin \theta$$

A boy and bicycle free-wheeling down a smooth slope inclined at 30° to the horizontal has an acceleration of $g \sin 30°$ or $9.8 \sin 30°$ m/s$^2$ about 5 m/s$^2$.

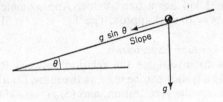

FIG. 18. Acceleration down slope

# FORCE, ACCELERATION, MOMENTUM

### Newton's Laws of Motion

1. Objects continue to remain at rest or to move in a straight line with constant velocity unless forces act on them.
   2. Force is proportional to the rate of change of momentum.
   3. Action and Reaction are equal and opposite.

*Inertia.* The first law implies that all objects have *inertia*. 'Mass' is a measure of the amount of inertia in an object. Masses are compared in terms of standard masses, such as the 'international prototype kilogram,' by chemical balances. In the absence of forces, for example, when friction is negligibly small as for an ice-puck, the latter continues to move in a straight line with practically constant velocity across plate glass. When a force acts on the puck, as in collision with a surrounding wooden frame, it changes its direction. On account of inertia, passengers continue to move forward when a car is brought suddenly to rest.

A small ball-bearing, dropped into a tall jar filled with glycerine, is observed to move with constant velocity after falling some distance. *Reason*: The frictional force increases with speed. At a particular velocity (*terminal velocity*), the frictional force plus liquid upthrust balances the downward weight of the ball-bearing. The resultant force is then zero. The ball-bearing thus continues to move with constant velocity.

*Force.*   1. Momentum = mass × velocity.

2. Force = momentum change *per second* = $\dfrac{\text{momentum change}}{\text{time}}$.

If mass is constant,

∴ force = mass × velocity change per second

∴ *force, F = mass (m) × acceleration (a)*

*Units.*   1. The *newton* is the force which gives a mass of 1 kilogramme an acceleration of 1 metre per second[2]. Symbol for 'newton' is 'N'.

2.1 *kilogramme force* (kgf) is the force due to gravity at a particular place on the earth. Unlike '1 kilogramme weight', which varies slightly over the earth, 1 kgf has a fixed value. Approximately, 1 kgf = 10 newtons, since $g = 10$ m/s[2] approx. The 'kgf' is not a SI unit.

## Trolley and Ticker-tape Experiments

In experiments to investigate the relation between force, mass and acceleration, (1) a trolley can be used as the mass, (2) a ticker-tape can be used to measure the acceleration, and (3) an elastic band, stretched by a given length, may provide a constant force. Frictional forces can always be eliminated. A long smooth board is tilted slightly until a tape attached to the trolley indicates uniform velocity when the trolley runs down the board. The effect of frictional forces is then neutralised by the trolley's weight and the board is then 'friction-compensated'.

(1) *To show a constant force produces a uniform acceleration.* Now attach a ticker-tape to the trolley T (Fig. 19 (*a*)). Allow T to run down an inclined board so that an acceleration is obtained. Remove the tape, cut it into successive strips of equal time-intervals, such as 5- or 10-ticks, paste them to represent a velocity–time graph (Fig. 19 (*b*)).

*Conclusion.*   Since the tops of the strips lie on a straight line, a constant force on the trolley produced a uniform acceleration. (*Note.* The constant force = component of trolley weight − friction.)

(2) *To show F ∝ a, mass constant.*   Place the two eyelets of an elastic band over the two pegs of a trolley (Fig. 20). Stretch the elastic by hand to a *fixed length* such as the wheels or other end of the trolley. With the trolley on a friction-compensated board (see above) and an attached ticker-tape, pull the trolley by the elastic, keeping the stretched length constant so that the force *F* is constant.

From the tape, determine the acceleration *a* (see p. 6). Repeat the experiment with two pieces of elastic *stretched by exactly the same length as before* so that the force *F* pulling the trolley is twice as much. Then with three pieces of elastic.

*Conclusion.*   *a ∝ F.*

(3) *To show how a depends on m for constant force.* (i) Keep force constant by using elastic stretched by same *length*, and (ii) vary *m* by using 1, 2,

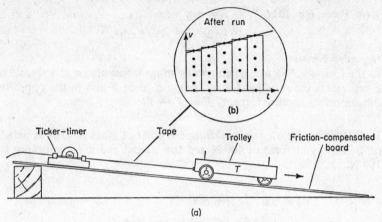

FIG. 19. Acceleration due to constant force

and 3 trolleys mounted on each other or by adding known masses to a trolley. Measure the acceleration *a* each time. By calculation, show that $a \propto 1/m$. General conclusion from (2) and (3): $F \propto ma$.

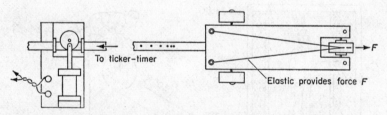

FIG. 20. Force and acceleration (friction-compensated board)

## Force Calculations

In using $F = ma$, when *m* is in kilogrammes (kg) and *a* in metre per second², then *F* is in *newtons* (N), the SI unit of force.

A practical unit of force is also the force due to gravity on a mass of 1 kg called 1 *kilogramme force* or 1 kgf. This gives the mass of 1 kg an acceleration *g* of about 10 m/s². But the force of 1 newton gives a mass of 1 kg an acceleration of 1 m/s², by definition. Thus 1 kgf = 10 newtons (approx.).

*Example.* Find (i) the force acting on a mass of 4 kg which gives it an acceleration of 2 m/s², (ii) the acceleration of an object of mass 2 kg when a force of 10 N acts on it.

(i) Force, $F = ma = 4$ (kg) $\times$ 2 (m/s$^2$)

$$= 8 \text{ N}.$$

(ii) Force, $F = 10$ N. From $F = ma$,

$$\therefore \ 10 = 2a \quad \text{or} \quad a = 5 \text{ m/s}^2.$$

## Opposing Forces

In the formula $F = ma$, when two or more forces act on a body, then $F$ represents the *resultant* force. Thus if a force $X$ acts in the opposite direction to a smaller force $Y$, $F = X - Y$.

1. *Friction as opposing force.* Suppose a car of mass 1000 kg is acted on by an engine force of 400 N and the ground and wind resistance is 100 N.

$F = (400 - 100) = 300$ N. From $F = ma$,

$$\therefore \ 300 \text{ (N)} = 1000 \text{ (kg)} \times a$$

$$\therefore \ a = \frac{300}{1000} = 0 \cdot 3 \text{ m/s}^2$$

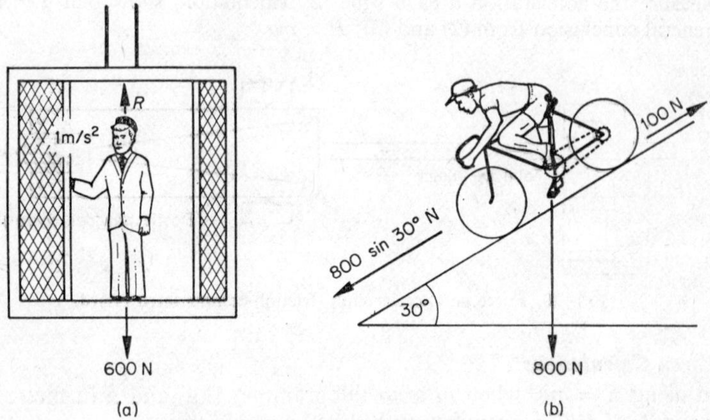

FIG. 21. Calculations on $F = ma$

2. *Weight as opposing force.* Suppose a lift rises with an acceleration of 1 m/s$^2$ and the reaction due to the floor on a man of mass 60 kg in the lift is required, assuming $g = 10$ m/s$^2$ (Fig. 21 (*a*)).

Suppose the upward reaction is $R$. The weight, acting downward, is 600 N.

$\therefore$ resultant upward force, $F = (R - 600)$ N. From $F = ma$,

$$\therefore \ (R - 600) = 60 \times 1$$

Solving, $\qquad \therefore \ R = 660 \text{ N}$

## Motion on Inclined Plane

When an object moves up or down a plane inclined at an angle $\theta$ to the horizontal, its weight $W$ has a component *down* the plane given by $W \sin \theta$.

*Example.* A rider and bicycle have a total mass of 80 kg (Fig. 21 (b)). When riding free-wheel down a slope at an angle of 30° to the horizontal, the resistance to the motion is 100 N. Calculate the acceleration down the plane (assume $g = 10 \text{ m/s}^2$).

Component of weight down plane $= 800 \sin 30° = 400 \text{ N}$,

$$\therefore \ \text{resultant force down plane, } F = (400 - 100)$$
$$= 300 \text{ N}$$

From $F = ma$,

$$\therefore \ 300 = 80a$$
$$\therefore \ a = 3\tfrac{3}{4} \text{ m/s}^2$$

## Circular Motion: Centripetal Force

An object moving in a circle with a constant speed $v$ has a velocity at B and at A directed along the respective tangents (Fig. 21A (a)). In Fig. 21A (b), the velocities are represented by PQ and RQ, since velocity is

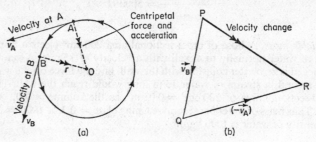

(a)           (b)

FIG. 21A. Motion in circle

a *vector*. The change or difference in velocity, $\vec{v}_B - \vec{v}_A = \vec{v}_B + (-\vec{v}_A) =$ PR. When A and B are very close to each other, PR is directed towards O, the *centre* of the circle. Hence

   (i) the acceleration is directed towards the centre,
  (ii) a *force*, called the *centripetal force*, acts towards the centre.

Calculation shows that the acceleration $= v^2/r$, where $r$ is the radius of the circle. Thus the centripetal force $F = ma = mv^2/r$.

*Examples.* For a stone whirled in a circle by a string, the centripetal force is the tension in the string. For a car moving round the circular track, the centripetal force is due to the frictional force between the wheels and ground. For a planet, such as the earth, moving round the sun, the centripetal force is the gravitational attraction between the sun and planet. Remember that the centripetal force, $mv^2/r$, always acts *towards* the centre of the circular path.

### Force and Linear Momentum

Force, $F$ = momentum change per second = $\dfrac{\text{momentum change}}{\text{time}}$

Momentum = mass × velocity. Thus:

(i) for constant mass, $F$ = mass × velocity change per second,
(ii) for constant velocity, $F$ = mass per second × velocity.

Units: If mass is in kg and velocity change in m/s, then $F$ is in *newtons*.

*Examples.* 1. *Constant mass.* A car of mass 1000 kg moving with a velocity of 36 km/h is brought to rest in 2 s in a collision test. Find the force on the car.

Velocity = 36 km/h = 10 m/s, mass = 1000 kg,

$\therefore$ force, $F$ = mass × velocity change per second

$$= \frac{1000 \times 10}{2} = 5000 \text{ N}$$

2. *Variable mass.* A hose of cross-sectional area 200 cm² ejects a horizontal stream of water normally to a wall with a velocity of 15 m/s. Assuming the water speed is zero after collision with the wall, find the force on the wall.

In 1 second, a stream of water 15 m long would reach the wall. This has a cross-sectional area of 200 cm² = 0·02 m², so the volume = 0·02 × 15 = 0·3 m³. Thus mass of water per second reaching plate = 0·3 × 1000 = 300 kg, since density of water is 1000 kg/m³

$\therefore$ $F$ = mass per second × velocity change

$$= 300 \times 15 = 4500 \text{ N}$$

3. *Gas pressure.* If a gas molecule has a mass $m$ and velocity $u$ when it strikes the wall of a containing vessel normally, and rebounds with an equal velocity $u$, then

$$\text{momentum change} = mu - (-mu) = 2mu$$

The pressure exerted by all the molecules is proportional to the average total momentum change per second, as explained on p. 43.

## Conservation of Linear Momentum

Momentum (mass × velocity) is a *vector* quantity; a mass of 50 g moving from left to right with a velocity of 10 cm/s has a momentum = 50 × 10 or 500 g cm/s in this direction. Another 100 g mass, moving with a velocity of 20 cm/s from *right* to *left*, has a momentum = −100 × 20 or −2000 g cm/s (note the minus). Their total momentum = 500 −2000 = −1500 g cm/s.

Collision experiments, such as those made by using a moving and stationary trolley, or a moving and stationary perspex model on a linear air-track, and other interaction experiments such as stationary trolleys set into motion by releasing a compressed spring, all show that: *When two or more bodies interact and no external forces are present, their total*

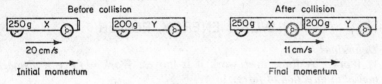

FIG. 22. Momentum conservation

*momentum in a given direction remains constant.* Thus suppose a moving trolley X, mass 250 g has a velocity of 20 cm/s before colliding with a stationary trolley Y of mass 200 g, and that after collision, X and Y stick together and move off with a velocity measured at 11 cm/s (Fig. 22). Then

$$\text{momentum of X and Y before collision} = 250 \times 20 = 5000$$

and

$$\text{momentum of X and Y after collision} = (250 + 200) \times 11 = 4950.$$

Thus, practically, the total linear momentum of the two trolleys before collision = their total momentum after collision.

*Calculations.* 1. A model aeroplane of total mass 2 kg emits burnt gases at the rear with a velocity of 60 m/s. If the mass of gas emitted in one second is 100 g, with what forward velocity will the model theoretically move at the end of this time?

Forward momentum of aeroplane = backward momentum of gas. Now mass of aeroplane = 2 kg − 100 g = 1900 g, velocity $v$, say; and mass of gas = 100 g, velocity 60 m/s

$$\therefore 1900v = 100 \times 60$$

$$\therefore v = \frac{100 \times 60}{1900} = 3 \text{ m/s (approx.)}$$

2. A ball *A* of mass 50 g moving with a velocity of 40 cm/s, collides with a ball *B* having a velocity 5 cm/s and moving in the opposite direction. If *A* and *B* stick together on collision and both move with a velocity of 20 cm/s in the direction of *A*, calculate the mass of *B*.

Momentum of *B* is opposite to that of *A*. Suppose *m* g is the mass of *B*,

∴ total momentum of *A* and *B* before collision = $50 \times 40 - m \times 5$

Total momentum after collision in same direction = $(50 + m) \times 20$,

$$\therefore 50 \times 40 - m \times 5 = (50 + m) \times 20$$
$$\therefore 2000 - 5m = 1000 + 20m$$
$$\therefore m = \frac{1000}{25} = 40 \text{ g}$$

# WORK, ENERGY, POWER

### Definitions

1. *Work.* A force does work if it moves. *Work = force × distance moved in direction of force.*

2. *Energy.* An object is said to have energy if it can do work.

3. *Kinetic Energy.* This is the energy possessed by an object by reason of its motion, e.g. a moving train.

4. *Potential Energy.* This is the energy possessed by reason of position or level, e.g. a coiled spring (molecules have displaced positions) or a pile-driver poised above the ground (gravitational energy). Note that 'energy' is a *scalar*—it is independent of direction.

5. *Power.* This is the rate of doing work or expending energy, so that power = work done/time.

### Unit of Work and Energy

Work and energy have the same units.

The *joule*, symbol J, is the work done when a force of 1 newton moves 1 metre in its own direction.

1 newton × 1 metre = 1 joule.

*Formulae.* (i) Work, $W = F \times s$, where *F* is the force and *s* is the displacement in the same direction as the force.

*F* in newtons and *s* in metres, then *W* is in *joules*.

(ii) *Kinetic energy*, K.E. = $\frac{1}{2}mv^2$, where *m* is the mass of the object moving with velocity *v*.

*m* in kg and *v* in m/s, then K.E. is in *joules*.

(iii) *Potential energy*, P.E. $= w \times h$, where $w$ is the weight of the object at a height $h$ above a particular reference level such as ground or sea level (note that $w = m \times g$; $w$ in N when $m$ in kg, $g = 10$ m/s²).

$w$ in *newton* and $h$ in m, then P.E. is in *joules*.

*Example.* A ball of mass 2 kg is released from A so that it rolls on a curved surface ABC (Fig. 23). The surface is smooth from A to B and rough from

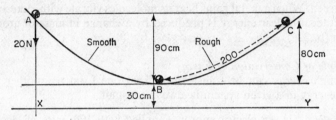

Fig. 23. Calculation

B to C. Calculate: (i) its potential energy at A relative to XY if the dimensions are those shown in Fig. 23, (ii) its kinetic energy at B, (iii) its velocity at B, (iv) the frictional force along BC if this length of the surface is 2 m and the ball comes to rest at C. (Assume $g = 10$ m/s².)

(i) P.E. at A = weight × height above XY
$$= 20 \text{ (N)} \times 1 \cdot 2 \text{ (m)} = 24 \text{ J}$$

since weight of 2 kg = 20 newtons (see above).

(ii) K.E. at B = loss in P.E. = weight × height moved
$$= 20 \text{ (N)} \times 0 \cdot 9 \text{ (m)} = 18 \text{ J}$$

(iii) $= \frac{1}{2}mv^2$, where $m$ in kg and $v$ in m/s,
$$\therefore \frac{1}{2} \times 2 \times v^2 = 18$$
$$\therefore v = \sqrt{18} = 4 \text{ m/s (approx.)}$$

(iv) Work done against frictional force, $F$ newtons,
$$= \text{loss in energy from B to C}$$
$$\therefore F \times 2 = \text{weight} \times \text{difference in height from C to A}$$
$$= 20 \text{ (N)} \times (0 \cdot 9 - 0 \cdot 8) \text{ (m)}$$
$$\therefore F = 1 \text{ N}$$

## Transformations of Energy

Steam engines change chemical energy, obtained by burning coal, to mechanical energy; a match which is struck on a rough surface changes mechanical to heat energy. An electric motor changes electrical to mechanical energy; a dynamo does the reverse. A microphone converts sound to electrical energy; a telephone earpiece or loudspeaker does the reverse. Electric lamp filaments convert electrical to heat and luminous energy; a photoelectric cell does the reverse.

Heat, light, sound, electrical, mechanical, chemical and nuclear energy are all different forms of energy. Heat radiation, light and chemical changes are due to energy changes of electrons in atoms or molecules. Sound is due to energy changes of atoms and molecules in the medium concerned. When a metal gains heat its molecules vibrate with increasing amplitude. Nuclear energy is produced by a change in mass of atomic nuclei (p. 206).

### Principle of Conservation of Energy

Although energy can be transformed from one form to another the total energy in a given system is always constant.

*Examples.* (1) An electric motor, supplied with 100 units of electric energy, may produce 80 units of mechanical energy, 5 units of heat energy in the wire, 12 units of heat energy due to friction at the bearings and 3 units due to sound energy. The total energy produced is still 100 units.

(2) A sledge poised at the top of an incline may then have 40 units of mechanical (potential) energy. When it reaches the bottom it may have 34 units of mechanical (kinetic) energy. During the run 5 units of heat energy may be produced in overcoming friction at the ground, and 1 unit of sound energy may be produced. Since the sledge has only 34 units of mechanical energy at the bottom of the incline compared with 40 units of mechanical energy at the top, the sledge cannot rise to the same height as before.

(3) If no mechanical energy is lost, as in an ideal case where no friction is present, the kinetic energy of the sledge at the bottom is equal to the potential energy at the top. Likewise, if a ball is dropped from a height and air friction is negligible, the kinetic energy gained = the potential energy lost. Thus if the ball has a mass of $m$ kg and falls a distance of 20 m, and the velocity is then $v$ m/s,

$$\text{kinetic energy gained} = \tfrac{1}{2}mv^2 = \text{loss in potential energy}$$

$$= m \times 10 \times 20 \text{ joules}$$

since $m$ kgf $= m \times 10$ newtons approx.

$$\therefore \tfrac{1}{2}mv^2 = 200m$$

$$\therefore v = \sqrt{400} = 20 \text{ m/s}$$

*Power*

Power, *P*, is the work done or energy expended per unit time,

$$\therefore P = \frac{\text{work done}}{\text{time taken}}$$

Unit: watt (= 1 joule per second, by definition). Symbol: **W**

1 horse-power (hp) = 0·75 kW (approx.)

*Example.* A car of mass 1000 kg is moving at constant velocity of 36 km/h against a resistance at the wheels of 900 N and air resistance of 1 per cent of the weight of the car. Estimate the engine power in kilowatts and horse-power.

Since the car is moving with constant velocity, resultant force on car = 0.

$\therefore$ force of engine = resistance of wheels and air

$$= 900 + \frac{1}{100} \times 10\ 000$$

$$= 1000\ \text{N}$$

Power = work done per second
    = force × distance moved per second
    = force × velocity
    = 1000 (N) × 10 (m/s)
    = 10 000 joule per second = 10 000 watts
    = 10 kW

But 1 hp = $\frac{3}{4}$ kW (approx.).

$$\therefore \text{power} = 13\cdot3\ \text{hp}$$

## STATICS

*Moments: Parallel Forces*

*Definition.* The *moment* of a force about a point or axis is the turning effect of the force about the point or axis and is measured by:

*force × perpendicular distance from point or axis to line of action of force*

Unit: Newton metre (N m)

Observe carefully that the *perpendicular* distance to the line of the force is required. In Fig. 24 a rope attached to one side of a trap-door with an axis O is pulled horizontally in the direction AL with a force *F* of 20 N; the moment about O = 20 N × 0·6 m = 12 N m. The moment of the weight *W*, 50 N, of the trap-door about O = 50 N × 0·4 m = 20 N m. The moment of *F* about O is thus less than the moment of *W* about O. The trap-door cannot be raised by *F*.

The maximum moment of $F$ about O is when $F$ is *perpendicular* to AO and acts along AC. Then moment = 20 N × OA = 20 N × 1 m = 20 N m. The trap-door is then just supported by $F$.

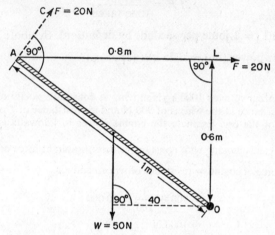

FIG. 24. Moments due to forces

A rope round a wheel of radius 0·5 metre, pulled tangentially to the wheel with a force of 10 newtons, has a moment about the centre of 10 newtons × 0·5 metre or 5 newton metre.

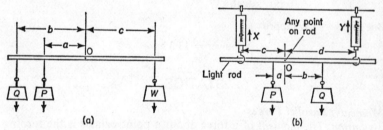

FIG. 25. Equilibrium of parallel forces

*Principle of Moments.*   When a pivoted rod is in equilibrium, the total clockwise moments about the fulcrum = the total anticlockwise moments about one fulcrum.

*Experiment.*   Suspend a light rod from O (Fig. 25 (*a*)). Move weights $P$, $Q$ and $W$ until the rod is in equilibrium. Measure the distances $a$, $b$, $c$ and note the values of $P$, $Q$ and $W$.

*Calculation.*   Total clockwise moment about O = $W \cdot c$. Total anticlockwise moment about O = $P \cdot a + Q \cdot b$. Compare $W \cdot c$ with $(P \cdot a + Q \cdot b)$.

## Conditions of Equilibrium of Parallel Forces

(1) The total forces in one direction = the total forces in the opposite direction. (2) The total clockwise moment of the forces about any point = the total anticlockwise moment about the same point.

*Experiment.* Suspend a light rod from the hooks of two spring balances and attach weights $P$ and $Q$ by strings (Fig. 25 (*b*)). Observe the readings $X$ and $Y$ of the upward forces on the rod, record the downward forces $P$ and $Q$, and measure the distances $a$, $b$, $c$ and $d$ of the four forces from *any* point O on the rod.

*Calculations.* (1) Total upward force = $X + Y$; total downward force = $P + Q$.

(2) Total clockwise moment about O = $X \cdot c + Q \cdot b$; total anticlockwise moment about O = $Y \cdot d + P \cdot a$. Compare (i) the upward and downward forces, (ii) the clockwise and anticlockwise moments.

*Examples.* 1. A uniform rod AB, of length 8 m and weight 7 N rests horizontally across two supports placed 6 m apart, one support being in contact with the end B of the rod (Fig. 26 (*a*)). Calculate the reactions at the supports. At what distance from O must a load of 8 N be suspended in order that the rod shall just leave the support at B? (*L.*)

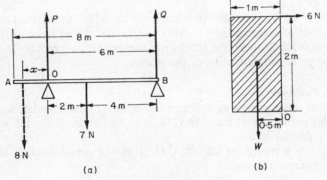

Fig. 26. Calculations on moments

(i) Suppose $P$, $Q$ are the reactions at the supports. Taking moments about B,

$$P \times 6 = 7 \times 4 \quad \text{or} \quad P = 4\tfrac{2}{3}\,\text{N}$$

$$\therefore Q = 7 - P = 2\tfrac{1}{3}\,\text{N}$$

(ii) When the rod just leaves the support at B, moment of 8 N about O = $7 \times 2$,

$$\therefore 8 \times x = 7 \times 2 = 14$$

$$\therefore x = 1\tfrac{3}{4}\,\text{m}$$

2. A heavy rectangular case has a cross-section 2 m by 1 m. A rope attached to the upper side is pulled parallel to the ground with a force of 6 newtons, and the case then just tilts about the lower edge at O (Fig. 26 (*b*)). Calculate the weight *W* of the case.

Take moments about O,

$$\therefore \ W \times 0{\cdot}5 \ (\text{m}) = 6 \ (\text{N}) \times 2 \ (\text{m})$$

$$\therefore \ W = 24 \ \text{N}$$

# CENTRE OF GRAVITY

### *Definition*
The centre of gravity, C.G., of a body is the point where the resultant weight of all the individual weights of its particles act.

The centre of mass, C.M., is the point where the resultant mass appears to act. This is the same place as the C.G. for small objects.

*Experiments.* (1) *Lamina.* Suspend the lamina from an axis through a hole in it, making sure the lamina swings freely. Use a plumbline to mark the vertical and repeat for another axis. The C.G. is the point of intersection of the two lines. Verify by balancing on the horizontal edge of a glass prism.

(2) *Stool.* Suspend the stool from one leg. Mark the vertical through the point of suspension by a string tied to the leg and to another point on the stool. Suspend the stool from another leg and repeat. The C.G. is the point of intersection of the strings.

### *C.G. Positions*
(1) For objects such as a disc, ring, square or rectangular, with the weight evenly distributed, the C.G. is at the centre or the intersection of the diagonals.

(2) For a triangular lamina, C.G. = two-thirds of distance along a median from any corner.

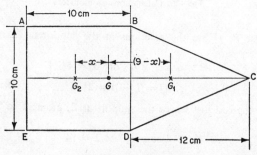

FIG. 27. C.G. calculation

*C.G. calculation.* Suppose a lamina ABCDE has its weight uniformly distributed as $w$ g per cm$^2$ and has the symmetrical shape shown in Fig. 27. We can divide it into a square ABDE and a triangle BCD. Then:

*Weight of square* = area $\times w = 100\,w$.   C.G. = $G_2$, where $G_2$ = 5 cm from BD.

*Weight of triangle* = area $\times w = \frac{1}{2}$ . 10 . 12$w$ = 60$w$.   C.G. = $G_1$, where $G_1 = \frac{1}{3} \times 12 = 4$ cm from BD.

The whole lamina can be balanced at is centre of gravity, G, which we suppose is $x$ cm from $G_2$. Now $G_1G = (9 - x)$ cm. Taking moments about G,

$$\therefore 100w \times x = 60w \times (9 - x)$$

Simplifying, $$\therefore x = \tfrac{54}{16} = 3 \cdot 4 \text{ cm (approx.)}$$

### Stability

1. *Stable Equilibrium.* Definition: An object is in stable equilibrium if, when slightly displaced and released, it returns to its original position.

Example: A cone or a cylinder standing on its base.

Explanation: If a cone is tilted slightly about an edge O of the base, the moment of the weight $W$ about O is an anticlockwise or restoring moment (Fig. 28 ($a$)).

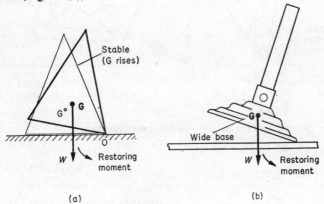

FIG. 28. Stable equilibrium

A bunsen burner has usually a heavy base so that its centre of gravity, G, is low (Fig. 28 ($b$)). When slightly displaced about an edge the vertical line through G falls *inside* the base and its moment restores the burner to its original position. A low C.G. helps to maintain stable equilibrium; racing cars are low.

Observe that the C.G. of an object in stable equilibrium *rises* when the object is slightly displaced.

2. *Unstable Equilibrium.* Definition: An object is in unstable equilibrium if, when slightly displaced and released, it moves farther away from its original position.

Example: A cone balanced on its apex (Fig. 29 (*a*)).

Explanation: If the cone is tilted slightly, the moment of its weight *W* about O is an anticlockwise or non-restoring moment (Fig. 29 (*a*)). The cone thus moves farther away and topples over. An inverted bunsen-burner may be unstable.

Unstable equilibrium tends to occur when the C.G. is high. The vertical through the C.G. then tends to fall *outside* the base when the object is slightly displaced. Observe that the C.G. of an object in unstable equilibrium *falls* when it is slightly displaced.

3. *Neutral Equilibrium.* Definition: An object is in neutral equilibrium if it remains in its new position when slightly displaced and released.

Example: A cone or cylinder lying on its curved side.

Explanation: The moment of the weight of the cone about the line of contact with the plane is zero when the cone is slightly displaced (Fig. 29 (*b*)). The cone hence remains in its new position. Observe that the C.G. remains at the *same* height when displaced.

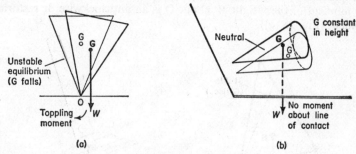

FIG. 29. Unstable and neutral equilibrium

*Machines*

*Definitions.* 1. Mechanical Advantage (M.A.) $= \dfrac{\text{Load } (W)}{\text{Effort } (P)}$.

2. Velocity Ratio (V.R.) $= \dfrac{\text{distance moved by effort } (x)}{\text{distance moved in same time by load } (y)}$.

3. Efficiency $= \dfrac{\text{work obtained from machine } (W \cdot y)}{\text{work done on or supplied to machine } (P \cdot x)}$.

*Note.* (*a*) Friction affects the mechanical advantage, but does *not* affect the velocity ratio.

(*b*) Efficiency $= \dfrac{\text{M.A.}}{\text{V.R.}}$, since efficiency $= \dfrac{W \cdot y}{P \cdot x} = \dfrac{W/P}{x/y}$.

On account of friction, M.A. is less than V.R. Ideally, with 100% efficiency, M.A. = V.R.

*Example* The efficiency of a machine is 80% and a load of 100 N is raised 1 m when the effort $F$ moves 5 m in its own direction. Calculate (i) the work obtained from the machine in joules, (ii) $F$, (iii) the mechanical advantage.

(i) Work obtained = load × distance = 100 (newtons) × 1 (metre)
    = 100 joules

(ii) Work supplied to machine = $F$ × 5 joules, if $F$ is in newtons,

$$\therefore \frac{100}{F \times 5} = 80\% = \frac{4}{5}$$

$$\therefore F = 25 \text{ N}$$

(iii) Mechanical advantage = $\dfrac{\text{Load}}{\text{Effort}} = \dfrac{100 \text{ N}}{25 \text{ N}} = 4$

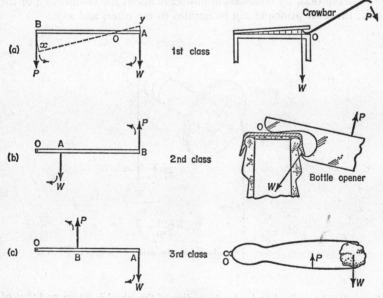

Fig. 30 Classes of levers

## Levers

The three classes are shown diagrammatically in Fig. 30. $P$ is the effort which overcomes the load $W$ by turning the lever about the fulcrum O. Note that $W$ is nearer O than $P$ except in the third class. Example of the *first class* are the crowbar (fulcrum at the bend) and scissors (fulcrum at the hinge); of the *second class*, the wheelbarrow (fulcrum at the wheel axle) and the bottle opener (fulcrum near the end); of the *third class*, sugar and coal tongs (fulcrum at the hinge).

*Velocity Ratio.*    If the effort moves a distance $x$ and the load a distance $y$, then, from similar triangles, $x/y = OB/OA = $ ratio of arms of lever. *Mechanical Advantage.*    Ideally, with no friction, $W/P = OB/OA$. A lever with a long effort 'arm' and a short load 'arm' has a high mechanical advantage.

### Wheel and Axle

The load, $W$, is attached to a rope round the *axle* of radius $r$. The effort $P$ is applied by a rope round the *wheel* of radius $R$ (Fig. 31). Suppose the wheel and axle are turned through one complete revolution. Then

$$\text{velocity ratio, V.R.} = \frac{2\pi R}{2\pi r} = \frac{R}{r}$$

Observe that, by considering moments about the central line of the axle, the lever principle can be applied to the wheel and axle.

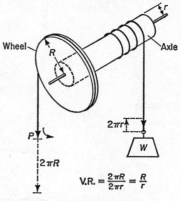

$$\text{V.R.} = \frac{2\pi R}{2\pi r} = \frac{R}{r}$$

FIG. 31. Wheel and axle

*Example.*    In a wheel and axle, the radius of the wheel is 30 cm and that of the axle is 5 cm. The machine has an efficiency of 60% and a bucket of water weighing 100 N is raised from a well 6 metres deep. Find (i) the work done in joules to raise the bucket directly without the machine, (ii) the work done by the effort in using the machine, (iii) the magnitude of the effort.

(i) Work done on bucket = weight × height moved
$$= 100 \text{ N} \times 6 \text{ m}$$
$$= 600 \text{ J}$$

(ii) If $W$ is the work done by effort, then, since work obtained/work supplied = efficiency,

$$\therefore \frac{600}{W} = 60\% = \frac{6}{10}$$

$$\therefore W = 1000 \text{ J}$$

(iii) Since $\qquad \dfrac{\text{M.A.}}{\text{V.R.}} = \text{efficiency} = \dfrac{6}{10}$

$$\therefore \text{M.A.} = \frac{6}{10} \times \frac{30 \text{ cm}}{5 \text{ cm}} = 3.6$$

$$\therefore \frac{100 \text{ N}}{\text{effort}} = 3.6$$

$$\therefore \text{effort} = \frac{100}{3.6} = 28 \text{ N}$$

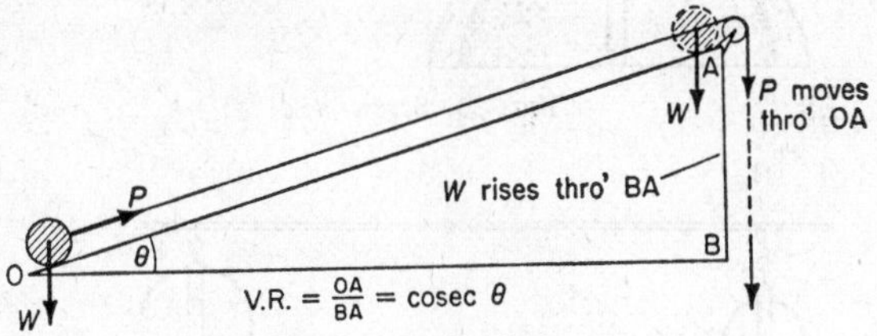

FIG. 32. Inclined plane

### Inclined Plane

Note that a load $W$ is raised a *vertical* distance BA while the effort moves a distance OA along the plane (Fig. 32). Thus:

$$\text{velocity ratio} = \frac{\text{OA}}{\text{BA}} = \frac{1}{\sin \theta} = \text{cosec } \theta$$

### Screw, Screw-jack

The *pitch*, $p$, of a screw is the distance its point moves forward when the screw is turned through one revolution. The pitch is the distance between successive threads. Thus if the pitch is 2 mm and the applied effort turns in a circle of radius 8 mm when a screw-driver is used, then

$$\text{velocity ratio} = \frac{2\pi \times 8}{2} = 25 \text{ (approx.)}$$

The *screw-jack*, used for raising heavy loads such as one side of a vehicle in changing wheels, has a screw T which raises the load (Fig. 33). When the effort, $P$, applied by the handle H, moves the nut N through one complete revolution, equal to a distance $2\pi \times$ radius or $2\pi \times 30$ cm say, the screw moves the load vertically through a distance equal to its pitch, say 3 mm or 0.3 cm. Thus velocity ratio $= 2\pi \times 30/0.3 = 630$ (approx.).

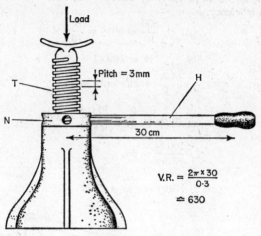

**Fig. 33. Screw-jack**

$$V.R. = \frac{2\pi \times 30}{0.3}$$

$$\simeq 630$$

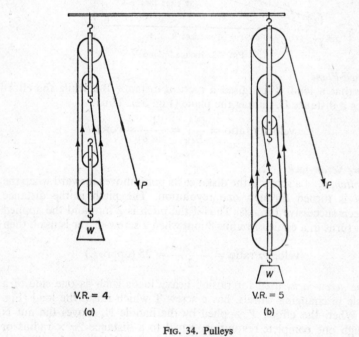

V.R. = 4

(a)

V.R. = 5

(b)

**Fig. 34. Pulleys**

## Pulleys

A 'block and tackle' system has a continuous rope round all the pulleys. For an even number of pulleys, the end of the rope is attached to the *upper* set of pulleys (Fig. 34 (*a*)); for an odd number of pulleys the end of the rope is attached to the *lower* set (Fig. 34 (*b*)). When the effort $P$ is applied, the load $W$ and the lower set of pulleys move up; the upper set remains fixed.

*Velocity Ratio.* If the load moves up a vertical distance $x$, the rope released on the two sides of the lowest pulley is $2x$. For two pulleys at top and bottom, the total length of rope released is $4x$. This is the distance moved down by $P$. Hence velocity ratio $= 4x/x = 4$. Generally, velocity ratio $= n$, where $n$ is the total number of pulleys.

*Mechanical Advantage.* This is affected both by the weight of the lower set of pulleys and by the frictional forces present. The greater the load $W$, the less is the relative effect of the weight of the pulleys and the frictional forces. Hence the *efficiency* of the system increases as the load increases.

### Measurement of Mechanical Advantage, Velocity Ratio, Efficiency

1. *Mechanical Advantage.* In any machine, use a known load as $W$, for example 500 g. Attach a scale-pan to the other end of the string, and add weights until $W$ rises steadily. The effort $P$ is the total weight of the scale-pan and weights added, for example 150 g. Calculate M.A. from $W/P$, which is $500/150$ or $5 \text{ N}/1.5 \text{ N} = 3.3$ in this case.

2. *Velocity Ratio.* Stand two vertical metre rulers beside the load $W$ and the effort $P$ respectively. Pull the string down through a distance $y$ cm, such as $40.0$ cm, and observe the distance $x$ moved up by $W$, such as $10.0$ cm.

Then velocity ratio $= 40.0/10.0 = 4$ in this case.

3. *Efficiency.* Calculate the work obtained from the machine from $W \times x$, which is $5 \text{ N} \times 0.1$ m or $0.5$ joule. Calculate the work supplied to the machine from $P \times y$, which is $1.5 \text{ N} \times 0.4$ m or $0.6$ joule. Then

$$\text{efficiency} = \frac{\text{work obtained}}{\text{work supplied}} = \frac{0.5}{0.6} \times 100\% = 83\% \text{(approx.)}$$

# PARALLELOGRAM AND TRIANGLE OF FORCES

*Resultant.* The *resultant* of two or more forces is the single force whose effect is equivalent in magnitude and direction to all the forces acting together.

*Equilibrant.* The *equilibrant* of two or more forces is the single force which keeps in equilibrium all the forces acting together.

*Parallelogram of Forces Principle.*    This is a law for finding the *resultant* of two forces. It states: If two forces, $P$ and $Q$, are represented in magnitude and direction by the respective sides OA and OC of a parallelogram OABC, their resultant is represented completely by the diagonal OB of the parallelogram passing through their point of intersection (Fig. 35 (*a*)).

*Verification.*    Join three pieces of string in a knot K. Attach two weights $P$ and $Q$ by passing them round grooved wheels (Fig. 35 (*b*)). Attach the third string to another weight $W$, which hangs vertically downwards.

When the strings and weights are all in equilibrium, (1) record the value of $P$ and $Q$ and (2) measure the angle LKN between the strings KL and KN,

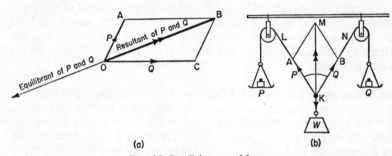

(a)                                   (b)

FIG. 35. Parallelogram of forces

which have tensions $P$ and $Q$ respectively in them. Now draw a parallelogram KAMB with $P$ and $Q$ to scale as two of its sides, and with the angle between them equal to angle LKN. Measure the diagonal KM, and find its magnitude from the scale used. It is practically equal to $W$. Now place the parallelogram drawing on the strings (Fig. 35 (*b*)), and observe that the direction of the diagonal MK is practically the same as that of $W$.

*Conclusion.*    $W$ is exactly equal and opposite to the resultant of $P$ and $Q$ because it maintains them both in equilibrium. Thus the diagonal KM represents the resultant in magnitude and direction.

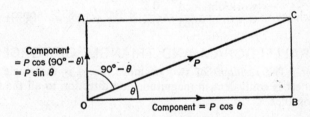

FIG. 36. Component of force

*Resolved Components.* From the parallelogram of forces, a single force $P$ can be resolved into two perpendicular *components*, each represented by the sides OB and OA of a rectangle OACB (Fig. 36). These components represent respectively the effective part of $P$ in the directions OB or OA. Each is given by:

$$resolved\ component = P \cos \theta$$

where $\theta$ is the angle between the direction and that of $P$. Thus a force of 80 N has a component of 80 N cos 60° in a direction inclined at 60° to the force, which is 40 N on calculation.

*Example.* A crate is dragged steadily in one direction along a horizontal floor by a rope which makes an angle of 30° with the floor in the vertical plane containing the direction of motion. If the tension in the rope is 100 N, find (*a*) the effective force on the crate along the floor, (*b*) the force tending to lift the crate.

(*a*) Effective force = component along floor
$$= 100 \cos 30° = 87 \text{ N (approx.)}$$

(*b*) Force tending to lift crate = vertical component
$$= 100 \sin 30° = 50 \text{ N}$$

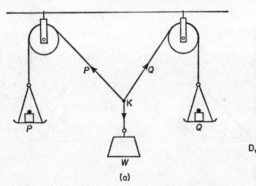

FIG. 37. Triangle of forces

## Triangle of Forces
*Principle.* This states: If three forces can be represented in magnitude and direction by the sides of a triangle take in order, then the three forces are in equilibrium.

*Verification.* Use three weights, *P, Q, W*, attached to three separate strings knotted at K as in (Fig. 37 (*a*)). When they are in equilibrium, obtain the directions of the forces *P, Q, W* in the three strings at K on a sheet of paper placed behind K. Alternatively, measure the angles between the strings with a protractor.

Then draw a line AB to represent $Q$ in magnitude and direction, a line BC to represent $P$ in magnitude and direction on the same scale, and a line CD from C to represent $W$ (Fig. 37 (b)). It will then be found that D and A practically coincide, so that a triangle is formed.

*Problems on Triangle of Forces Principle.*   In problems on finding one or more unknown forces when three forces keep an object in equilibrium, note the following:

(1) A smooth surface exerts a reaction (force) on an object resting on it which is always *perpendicular to the surface.*

(2) The three forces must all pass through one point. Thus if the directions of two are known, the third force passes through their point of intersection.

(3) If two forces are known, the third force may be found by drawing the parallelogram of forces, because it is equal and opposite to their resultant.

(4) If one force is known, the other two can be found by first drawing this force to scale in magnitude and direction. The triangle of forces is then completed by drawing lines from the two ends parallel to the other two forces.

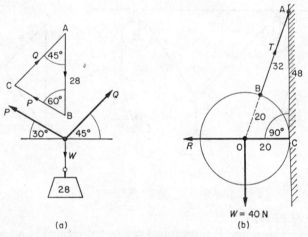

(a)     (b)

FIG. 38. Calculations

*Examples of three forces in equilibrium.*  1. A 28 N weight is suspended by two strings attached to it and inclined at 30° and 45° respectively to the horizontal. Find the pull in each string. How should the strings be arranged so that the pull in each is as small as possible? (*L.*)

Suppose $P$, $Q$ are the respective tensions in the two strings (Fig. 38 (a)). Draw AB vertically to scale to represent 28·0 N. Then draw a line from B parallel to the direction of $P$ and a line from $A$ parallel to the direction of $Q$ to intersect at C. Then ABC is the triangle of forces. By scale drawing,

$$P = 20.5 \text{ N}, \quad Q = 25.1 \text{ N}$$

The horizontal components of $P$ and $Q$ do not help to support the vertical weight. Thus the pull in each is as small as possible if both strings are vertical.

2. A sphere of mass 4·0 kg is suspended from a point A on a smooth wall and makes contact at C (Fig. 38 (b)). The string is attached at B, and AC is 48 cm, AB is 32 cm and the radius OC is 20 cm. Find the tension $T$ in the string and the reaction $R$.

The three forces acting on the ball, $T$, the weight $W$, and the reaction $R$ normal to the wall, must all pass through one point. The weight $W$ and $R$ pass through O, the centre of the ball. Hence the line of $T$, which is AB, passes through O. Starting with $W = 40$ N, the triangle of forces can be drawn to find $T$ and $R$. Results show that $T = 43$ N and $R = 17$ N.

# PRESSURE IN FLUIDS

*Definition*
*Pressure* is the average *force per unit area* at the place concerned. (Observe that 'pressure' is not a 'force'.)
Units: Newton per metre² (N/m²). Note that $10^6$ N/m² $= 1$ N/mm². 1 bar $= 10^5$ N/m² $= 0.1$ N/mm².

*Formulae.*   Average pressure, $p = \dfrac{\text{force, } F}{\text{area, } A}$,

or                          force (thrust), $F = p \times A$

*Example.*   A solid box weighting 120 newtons has dimensions 0·5 m by 1 m by 0·2 m. Calculate the greatest and least pressure which can be exerted on a flat surface by the box.

Greatest pressure is exerted when the area in contact with the surface is least.

$$\therefore \text{ greatest pressure} = \frac{120 \text{ N}}{0.5 \times 0.2 \text{ m}^2} = 1200 \text{ N/m}^2$$

$$\text{Least pressure} = \frac{120 \text{ N}}{0.5 \times 1 \text{ m}^2} = 240 \text{ N/m}^2$$

*Pressure at a Depth.*        Pressure, $p = h \rho g$

where $h$ is the depth and $\rho$ is the density of the fluid.

*Proof of $p = h\rho$.* Consider a horizontal area $A$ at a depth $h$. The force or thrust acting down is the weight of fluid above it. Now the volume of fluid above it $= A \times h$, and hence the mass $= A \times h \times \rho$. The weight (force) $=$ mass $\times g$, where $g$ is the acceleration due to gravity. See p. 17.

$$\therefore p = \frac{\text{weight}}{\text{area}} = \frac{A \times h \times \rho \times g}{A} = h\rho g$$

*Units.* When $h$ is in m, $\rho$ in $kg/m^3$, $g = 9.8$ m/s$^2$, then $p$ is in N/m$^2$.

*Examples.* 1. At the bottom of a *column of mercury* 760 mm (0·76 m) high, density 13,600 kg/m$^3$,

$$\text{pressure, } p = h\rho g = 0.76 \times 13,600 \times 9.8 \text{ N/m}^2$$
$$= 101,300 \ (1.013 \times 10^5) \text{ N/m}^2$$
$$= 1.013 \text{ bar} = 1013 \text{ millibars}$$

2. At the bottom of a *column of air* 2 kilometres high and average density 1·2 kg/m$^3$,

$$\text{pressure, } p = h\rho g = 2000 \times 1.2 \times 9.8 \text{ N/m}^2$$
$$= 24,000 \text{ N/m}^2 \text{ (approx.)}$$

3. At a place 100 m below *water*, density 1000 kg/m$^3$

$$\text{pressure, } p = h\rho g = 100 \times 1000 \times 9.8 = 980,000 \text{ N/m}^2$$

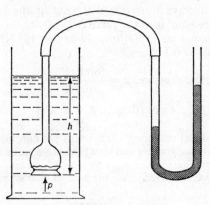

Fig. 39. Pressure and depth

*Experiments.* A thistle funnel, covered with thin rubber or a plastic membrane and connected to a manometer, can be lowered into a liquid to show (i) pressure increases with depth, (ii) the pressure at a given place is the same in all different directions, (iii) pressure increases with density (Fig. 39).

To show pressure is *directly proportional to depth h*, lower an open glass tube T into water with a flat plastic cover C held against the lower end (Fig. 40 (*a*)). Now pour a light oil into T until C just floats away, as shown. Measure the height $H$ of the oil and the depth $h$ of the water.

The pressure at $h$ due to the water is directly proportional to the weight $W$ of oil, which itself is proportional to $H$. Plot $H$ v. $h$. The result is a straight line passing through the origin (Fig. 40 (b)). This shows that pressure is directly proportional to $h$.

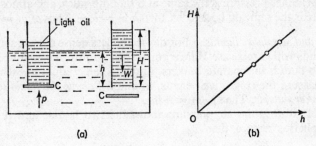

(a)     (b)

Fɪɢ. 40. Experiment to show $p \propto$ depth

*Hydraulic Press.* This is a machine which uses the principle that *pressure is transmitted equally throughout a liquid.* By using a lever, a narrow piston of small area $a$ exerts a pressure $p$ on a liquid. This is transmitted to a wide piston of large area $A$ which compresses a load.

*Velocity Ratio.* Volume of liquid transferred from small to large piston side is the same. Thus

$a \times$ distance moved by small piston $(x)$
$$= A \times \text{distance moved by large piston } (y)$$

$$\therefore \frac{x}{y} = \text{velocity ratio} = \frac{A}{a}$$

Neglecting friction, force applied, $P = pa$, and load or weight overcome, $W = pA$. Hence mechanical advantage $= pA/pa = A/a$, if the machine is 100% efficient, but in practice it is much less.

*Example.* A hydraulic press has pistons of cross-sectional area 100 cm² and 50,000 cm² respectively. The machine is 80% efficient and a force of 10 N is applied. What is the load overcome?

$$\text{Velocity ratio, V.R.} = \frac{A}{a} = \frac{50\,000 \text{ cm}^2}{100 \text{ cm}^2} = 500$$

Now
$$\text{efficiency} = \frac{\text{M.A.}}{\text{V.R.}} = \frac{80}{100}$$

$$\therefore \text{M.A.} = \frac{80}{100} \times \text{V.R.} = \frac{80}{100} \times 500 = 400$$

$$\therefore \frac{W}{10 \text{ N}} = 400 \quad \text{or} \quad W = 4000 \text{ N}$$

*Density or Relative Density: Oil and Water.* For oil and water, or liquids which do not mix, (i) pour water into an open U-tube and (ii) pour oil in one side only. Measure $h_1$ and $h_2$, the heights of water and oil above the *surface of separation* S. Then $\rho_2/\rho_1 = h_1/h_2$.

Proof: Since pressure is the same at S on both sides, and atmospheric pressure is the same on both sides, then $h_1\rho_1 = h_2\rho_2$. Thus $\rho_2/\rho_1 = h_1/h_2$.

*Dense and less dense liquids.* For dense and less dense copper sulphate, or liquids which mix, use Hare's apparatus, an inverted U-tube. Place the two liquids in separate beakers, draw up some liquid in each limb, and measure the respective heights, $h_1$ and $h_2$, *above the liquid level in the beaker outside.* Then $\rho_2/\rho_1 = h_1/h_2$.

Proof: If $B$ is the air pressure above the two liquids and $A$ is the atmospheric pressure, then

$$A = B + h_1\rho_1 = B + h_2\rho_2$$

$$\therefore \rho_2/\rho_1 = h_1/h_2$$

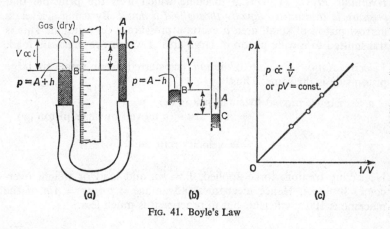

FIG. 41. Boyle's Law

## Pressure in Gases

*Boyle's Law.* This states: For a fixed mass of gas at constant temperature, $pV = $ constant, where $p$ is the pressure and $V$ is the volume, *or pressure is inversely-proportional to the volume ($p \propto 1/V$).*

*Experiment.* Use dry air trapped by a mercury column in a tube DB of uniform cross-sectional area (Fig. 41 (*a*)). Move the side C up to increase the pressure and down to decrease the pressure. Take five or six readings of volume, $V$, proportional to $l$, and of pressure $p$. This is $(A + h)$ mm mercury when C is above B (Fig. 41 (*a*)), and $(A - h)$ mm mercury when C is below B (Fig. 41 (*b*)), $A$ being atmospheric pressure.

*Calculation.* Work out the product $p \times V$, or $l \times p$, and see if this is constant. Alternatively, plot $p$ v. $1/V$; this will lie on a straight line passing through the origin, showing $p$ is inversely-proportional to $V$ (Fig. 41 (c)).

*Bourdon Gauge Method.* This gauge is one which reads directly pressures greater than atmospheric pressure. Using oil, air is trapped in a *wide uniform* tube, with a scale behind for reading its volume. Various pressures, $p$, and volumes, $V$, are thus easily read directly—a foot pump transmits pressures through the oil to the trapped air.

*Kinetic Theory Explanation of Boyle's Law.* Gas pressure is due to the continual rapid bombardment of the molecules on the walls of the container.

Assuming elastic collision, suppose a molecule of mass $m$ strike a wall of a containing cube perpendicularly with a velocity $u$. It then rebounds with a velocity $-u$. The *momentum change* $= mu - (-mu) = 2mu$. (Note that the momentum change is proportional to $u$.)

To find the number of collisions per second, suppose the length of the cube is $l$. Then time to cross from one wall to opposite side and back $= 2l/u$. (Note the time between collisions is proportional to $1/u$.)

$$\therefore \text{ rate of change of momentum} = \frac{2mu}{2l/u} = \frac{mu^2}{l}$$

Since $m$ and $l$ are constant, and the rate of change of momentum is the *force* on the wall, then force $\propto u^2$. Hence

$$\text{pressure} \propto u^2$$

If we take *all* the molecules into account, which have different speeds, then *pressure is proportional to the mean (average) of the squares of the speeds.*

Suppose the volume of the gas is halved by pushing down a piston in a container of a rectangular cross-section. Then (i) the same momentum change, proportional to $u$, occurs at each impact, but (ii) the impacts occur *twice* as fast, since the molecules take half the time between successive impacts. Thus pressure is double when volume is halved.

*Calculations on Boyle's law.* 1. A uniform capillary tube, open at one end and sealed at the other, has a mercury thread inside, 10·0 cm long, which traps some air. Placed horizontally on a table, the length of the air column is 8·6 cm (Fig. 42 (a)). Placed vertically with the open end at the top, the length of the air column is now 7·6 cm (Fig. 42 (b)). Calculate the atmospheric pressure. What is the new length of the air column when the capillary tube is inverted? (Fig. 42 (c)).

(i) Suppose $A$ = atmospheric pressure in cm mercury. Then (1) *horizontally,* pressure of air $= A$, (2) *vertically*, pressure of air $= A + 10$ (Fig. 42 (a), (b)). From Boyle's law, $pV = $ constant,

$$\therefore A \times 8 \cdot 6 = (A + 10) \times 7 \cdot 6$$

$$\therefore 8 \cdot 6A - 7 \cdot 6A = 76 \quad \text{or} \quad A = 76 \text{ cm mercury}$$

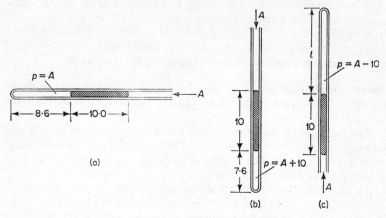

FIG. 42. Calculation

(ii) When the capillary tube is inverted, the weight of the mercury thread *opposes* the air pressure (Fig. 42 (c)). Hence the new air pressure $= A - 10$ $= 76 - 10 = 66$. Suppose new air column is $l$ cm. Then, from Boyle's law,

$$66 \times l = A \times 8 \cdot 6 = 76 \times 8 \cdot 6$$

$$\therefore l = \frac{76 \times 8 \cdot 6}{66} = 9 \cdot 9 \text{ cm}$$

*Atmospheric Pressure.* Classroom demonstrations: (1) collapsing can —air pumped out of a tin can leads to collapse of can, (2) Magdeburg hemispheres—air pumped out of sealed hemispheres, when hemispheres can no longer be pulled apart. In each case force $=$ air pressure $\times$ area, and air pressure is about $0 \cdot 1 \text{ N/mm}^2$, so that a horizontal area of $300 \text{ mm}^2$ (this page) has a force of 30 N on it due to air pressure.

*Simple Barometer.* Take a barometer (thick-walled) tube about a metre long, fill it nearly to the top with clean mercury (Fig. 43 (a)), and then invert it a few times so that the air bubble runs along and collects the small trapped air-bubbles in the mercury. Finally fill the tube to the brim, so that air is completely excluded. With one finger on the top, completely invert the barometer tube in a trough of mercury so that the top is below the liquid level. Remove the finger. The mercury level falls to about 76 cm (760 mm) above the level in the trough (Fig. 43 (b)). Fix the tube vertically in a clamp. Place a vertical metre rule to just touch the mercury, as shown—a short distance away avoids the meniscus curve near the glass. The height of mercury in the barometer tube above the outside level can now be measured.

*Testing for Faulty Vacuum.* Tilt the barometer tube. If the *vertical* height above the mercury level in the trough does not drop, there is no air at the top. Or, tilt the tube more and more until the vertical height of the closed end is less than 76 cm above the mercury in the trough as at X in (Fig. 43 (b)). If the mercury does not completely fill the space in the tube, air is present, as shown.

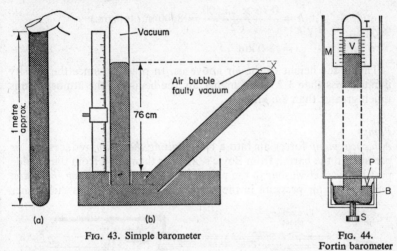

FIG. 43. Simple barometer

FIG. 44.
Fortin barometer

*Fortin Barometer.* This has (1) a barometer tube T with a vacuum above it, (2) a short metal scale M reading from 70–85 cm for example, and an adjustable vernier scale V, (3) a fixed ivory index P at the base which is the zero of the metal scale, (4) a leather bag B as a reservoir in which the mercury level can be adjusted by an external screw S pressing on the bottom. Fig. 44.

To measure atmospheric pressure, first turn S until the tip of P just touches the mercury level in B. Then measure the height of the mercury in the tube by moving the vernier until it is just level with the meniscus.

*Air Pressure Calculations.* Air pressure can be expressed in (1) mm of mercury (mmHg), or (2) torr (1 torr = 1 mmHg) or (3) millibars.

Suppose the height is 760 mmHg, called *standard (normal) atmospheric pressure*. Then, since $h = 0.76$ m, $\rho = 13,600$ kg/m$^3$, $g = 9.8$ m/s$^2$,

$$p = h\rho g = 0.76 \times 13,600 \times 9.8 \text{ N/m}^2$$
$$= 1.013 \times 10^5 \text{ N/m}^2$$

Since $10^5 \text{ N/m}^2 = 1$ bar, $100 \text{ N/m}^2 = 1$ millibar.

$$\therefore \text{ atmospheric pressure} = 1013 \text{ millibars (mb)}$$

From Boyle's law, the air at the ground is compressed more than air higher up and therefore has a greater density. Suppose, however, we assume that air has a constant density of $1 \cdot 2 \text{ kg/m}^3$. Then the height $h$ of this air which exerts the same pressure at its base as a column of mercury 760 mm or 0·76 m high is given by

$$h \times 1 \cdot 2 \times g = 0 \cdot 76 \times 13{,}600 \times g$$

$$\therefore h = \frac{0 \cdot 76 \times 13{,}600}{1 \cdot 2} = 8600 \text{ m (approx.)}$$

$$= 8 \cdot 6 \text{ km}$$

This is the height of the air above us. In practice, since the density is much less than $1 \cdot 2 \text{ kg/m}^3$ higher up, the height of the atmosphere is much greater than 8·6 km.

### Pumps

A *bicycle pump* forces air into a tyre. *Raising the piston* reduces the air pressure in the barrel, from Boyle's law. Air then flows from the outside past the leather washer in the piston into the barrel. *Pushing the piston forward,* the air pressure in the barrel increases and forces the washer

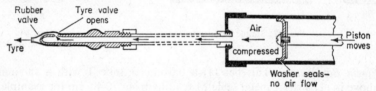

FIG. 45. Bicycle pump

against the sides of the barrel, thus forming a seal (Fig. 45). The air is then forced through the valve in the tyre, which opens, into the bicycle inner tube.

*Common Pump.* This has a valve A in the pipe at the foot of the barrel and a valve B in the piston. When the pump is working the valves open and shut alternately.

*Piston up,* valve A opens and B shuts—the external atmospheric pressure pushes water into the pipe in the ground which flows past A. *Piston down,* A closes due to the thrust of water above it and the water is then forced past B which opens. When the piston is now raised, water is carried up the barrel and flows through the outlet.

*Limitation.* Atmospheric pressure supports theoretically a height of about 34 ft of water. The height is much less than 34 ft in practice. The depth of water raised is thus limited with this type of pump.

*Force Pump.* This can *force* water to heights greater than 34 ft. It has a foot valve A and a side valve B. *Piston up,* valve A opens, B shuts and atmospheric pressure pushes water past A. *Piston down,* valve A shuts, and valve B opens—the height of water expelled depends on the downward thrust of the piston. *Air dome*—air is compressed when piston is pushed down, and the pressure expels water past B on upstroke of piston. Thus water is forced through the outlet on both strokes of the pump when an air dome is present.

## FORCES DUE TO FLUIDS

### Fluids at Rest

*Archimedes' Principle.* This states: *The upthrust on an object immersed in a fluid is equal to the weight of fluid displaced.*

Observe that (i) an 'upthrust' is a force—it is measured in newtons, (ii) a 'fluid' is a liquid or gas, (iii) an object fully immersed in a fluid displaces its own volume.

*Verification of Archimedes' Principle.* *Method.* (i) Weigh a large object O such as a stone or light metal with a spring balance—suppose it is 0·94 N (Fig. 46). Now note the new reading on the balance when O is

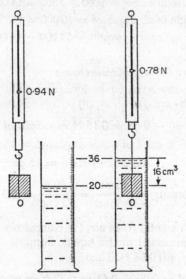

FIG. 46. Archimedes' Principle

completely immersed inside water in a measuring cylinder—suppose it is 0·78 N, (iii) observe the initial reading (20 cm³) and final reading (36 cm³) of the water level in the cylinder.

*Calculation.*   Upthrust = weight in air − apparent weight in water = 0·94 − 0·78 = 0·16 N. Weight of water displaced = weight of (36 − 20) or 16 cm³ of water = weight of 16 g = 0·16 N.

*Conclusion.*   Upthrust on O = weight of liquid displaced by O.

*Some Calculations using Archimedes' principle.*   **1.** A metal weighs 0·40 N in air. What is the apparent weight when fully immersed in water if its density is 8 g/cm³?

To find the upthrust, always determine the *volume* first. Thus

$$\text{volume of metal} = \frac{\text{mass}}{\text{density}} = \frac{40 \text{ g}}{8} = 5 \text{ cm}^3$$

∴ upthrust = weight of 5 cm³ of water = 5 × 0·01 N = 0·05 N

∴ apparent weight = weight in air − upthrust = 0·40 − 0·05 = 0·35 N

**2.**   A balloon of volume 10 000 m³ is filled with hydrogen of density 0·09 kg/m³. The mass of the balloon material and apparatus inside is 500 kg. Calculate the uplift on the balloon if the density of air is 1·2 kg/m³.

$$\text{Mass of hydrogen} = 10\,000 \times 0.09 = 900 \text{ kg}$$
$$\therefore \text{total weight} = 9000 + 5000 = 14\,000 \text{ N}$$
$$\textit{Upthrust} = \text{weight of air displaced} = 10\,000 \times 1.2 \times 10 = 120\,000 \text{ N}$$
$$\therefore \text{uplift} = \text{upthrust} - \text{weight} - 12\,000 - 14\,000 = 106\,000 \text{ N}$$

### Density or Relative Density Measurements

1. *Solid.*   Weigh the solid (i) in air, (ii) totally immersed in water. Suppose the results are (i) 0·80 N, (ii) 0·65 N. Then

$$\text{upthrust} = 0.80 - 0.65 = 0.15 \text{ N} = \text{weight of displaced water}$$
$$\therefore \text{mass of water displaced} = 15 \text{ g}$$
$$\therefore \text{volume of solid} = 15 \text{ cm}^3$$

$$\therefore \text{density} = \frac{\text{mass}}{\text{volume}} = \frac{80 \text{ g}}{15 \text{ cm}^3} = 5.3 \text{ g/cm}^3$$

2. *Liquid.*   Weigh a solid (i) in air, (ii) completely immersed in water, (iii) completely immersed in the liquid. Suppose the readings are (i) 0·90 N, (ii) 0·72 N, (ii) 0·68 N. Then

upthrust in liquid = 0·90 − 0·68 = 0·22 N = wt of liquid displaced, and

$$\text{upthrust in water} = 0\cdot90 - 0\cdot72 = 0\cdot18 \text{ N}$$
$$= \text{wt. of } equal\ volume \text{ of water displaced}$$

(Note that the volumes of liquid and water are both equal to the volume of the solid used. Any solid may be used provided it does not dissolve.)

Since mass of liquid displaced $= 22$ g,

$$Density \text{ of liquid} = \frac{\text{mass}}{\text{volume}} = \frac{22 \text{ g}}{18 \text{ cm}^3} = 1\cdot2 \text{ g/cm}^3$$

### Principle of Flotation

This states: *When an object floats, its weight is equal to the weight of fluid displaced.* This is true because (i) the weight of the floating object is balanced by the upthrust of the fluid, (ii) the upthrust $=$ the weight of fluid displaced from Archimedes' principle.

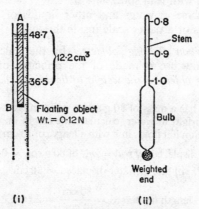

FIG. 47. (i) Flotation (ii) Hydrometer

*Verification.* Weigh a narrow object such as a piece of wood A weighted at one end. Suppose it is $0\cdot12$ N. Now float it in water in a burette B, taking the initial reading of the level, say $36\cdot5$ cm³, and the final level, $48\cdot7$ cm³ (Fig. 47 (i)).

*Calculation.* Weight of water displaced $=$ wt of $(48\cdot7 - 36\cdot5)$ cm³ $= 0\cdot122$ N. Weight of floating object $= 0\cdot12$ N.

*Conclusion.* Allowing for experimental error, weight of object $=$ weight of liquid displaced.

*Hydrometer.* This consists of (i) a narrow graduated stem—this makes the instrument more sensitive because small differences in density then produce large changes in the readings on the stem, (ii) a wide bulb—this ensures sufficient upthrust to counterbalance the hydrometer weight, (iii) a weighted end—this ensures stability in the liquid (Fig. 47 (ii)). Observe that the density readings on the stem increase upwards.

*Principle.* Suppose the hydrometer weighs 0·40 N. In water, density 1 g per cm³, it sinks until the volume displaced is 40 cm³, from principle of flotation. In oil of density 0·8 g per cm³, it sinks until the volume displaced = 40/0·8 = 50 cm³, because 50 cm³ of oil weighs 0·40 N. The hydrometer thus *sinks more* in a less dense liquid. In a denser liquid, for example 2 g per cm³, the volume displaced is 20 cm³, which is *less* than in water. The hydrometer stem can thus be calibrated with density readings, corresponding to the level of the liquid in which it floats.

*Simple Hydrometer.* This could be either (i) a drinking straw with one end closed by sealing wax, or (ii) a test-tube flattened at the lower end and filled here with lead shot.
*Calibration.* Immerse in water and other liquids of known density, using rubber bands or a paper scale inside the tube.

*Some calculations on floating objects.* In the calculations which follow, observe how use is made of the principle of flotation: *The weight of a floating object = the weight of liquid displaced.*

1. A rod of wood has a mass of 80 g and a uniform cross-sectional area of 4 cm². If it floats upright in water, calculate the length immersed. Calculate the density of a solution if it floats in it with a length of 16 cm immersed.

Weight of water displaced by rod = wt. of 80 g rod = 0·8 N

$\therefore$ volume of water displaced = 80 cm³

$$\therefore \text{length immersed} = \frac{80 \text{ cm}^3}{4 \text{ cm}^2} = 20 \text{ cm}$$

In a solution of density $\rho$, mass of liquid displaced

$$= \text{volume} \times \text{density} = 16 \times 4 \times \rho$$

$$\therefore 16 \times 4 \times \rho = 80 \quad \text{or} \quad \rho = 1·25 \text{ g/cm}^3$$

2. A sinker of mass 40 g and density 4 g/cm³ is attached to some cork of mass 10 g. Both together just float fully immersed in water. Calculate the density of the cork.

$$\text{Volume of sinker} = \frac{40}{4} = 10 \text{ cm}^3$$

$$\text{Volume of cork} = \frac{\text{mass}}{\text{density}} = \frac{10}{\rho} \text{ cm}^3$$

where $\rho$ is the density in g/cm³.

$$\therefore \text{ total volume} = \left(10 + \frac{10}{\rho}\right) \text{cm}^3$$

$$\therefore \text{ upthrust} = \left(10 + \frac{10}{\rho}\right) \times 0.01 \text{ N} = (0.40 + 0.10) \text{ N}$$

$$\therefore 10 + \frac{10}{\rho} = 50 \quad \text{or} \quad \rho = 0.25 \text{ g/cm}^3$$

3. A hydrometer of mass 20 g floats with 8 cm of its stem not immersed in water. The area of the uniform stem is 1 cm$^2$. What length of stem us not immersed when the hydrometer is placed in oil of density 0·8 g/cm$^3$?

Upthrust on hydrometer = weight of mass 20 g

$\therefore$ volume immersed in water = 20 cm$^3$

In oil, upthrust = 20 × 0·01 N = $V$ × 0·8 × 0·01 N, where $V$ is volume immersed.

$$\therefore V = \frac{20}{0.8} = 25 \text{ cm}^3$$

$\therefore$ additional volume immersed = 25 − 20 = 5 cm$^3$

$\therefore$ additional length immersed = 5 cm

$\therefore$ length not immersed = 8 − 5 = 3 cm

## Fluids in Motion

*Bernoulli's Principle.* Water moving steadily along a horizontal pipe has a greater velocity where the cross-section is narrow. This is because the volume per second (*area × distance per second*) is the same at each part.

Assuming negligible viscosity, so that no work is spent on overcoming friction, then the work done per unit volume of water by the excess pressure = gain in kinetic energy of the water. The excess pressure pushes the water from a place X of high pressure to a place Y of low pressure. Since there is a *gain* in kinetic energy, it follows that the velocity of the water at Y is greater than at X. Generally, *the pressure in a fluid is low where the velocity is high,* and *high where the velocity is low.* This was first deduced in mathematical form by *Bernoulli.* The conditions are (i) the viscosity of the fluid is negligible, (ii) the fluid flows steadily in streamline or 'laminar' flow.

*Demonstration.* Pass a steady flow of water through horizontal glass tubes with varying cross-section and with vertical tubes attached to show the pressure variation. At the wide sections, where the velocity is high, the pressure is seen to be less than at narrow sections, where the velocity is lower.

*Applications.*   1. *Filter pump.*   When the pump F is connected to a tap, water flows faster through a narrow section near the middle. This reduces the air pressure here. Air then flows from the apparatus connected to the pump and is swept away by the water (Fig. 48 (*a*)).

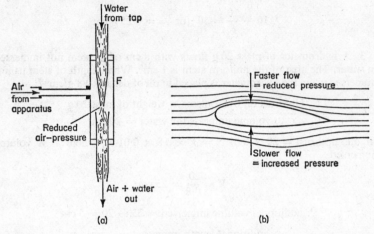

FIG. 48. Bernoulli's Principle

2. *Aerofoil lift.*   Air flows faster on the upper side of the aerofoil A— observe the closeness of the streamlines compared with those below. The air pressure below is hence greater than that above, thus providing lift (Fig. 48 (*b*)).

# 2    Matter and Molecules

*Matter*
Solids, liquids, gases—consists of minute particles, *molecules*, having an independent existence.

*Existence of Molecules*
Shown (i) indirectly by Brownian movement or motion, (ii) directly by photographs taken by high-power microscopes.

*Brownian Movement* is the random motion of very small particles in a liquid or gas due to bombardment by the molecules.

*To Demonstrate.*    (i) In liquids, use well-diluted aquadag or photopake, which contain fine particles, (ii) in gases, use fine particles from burnt cord or tobacco smoke. The cell A with cover slip is illuminated from the side by a source B and lens D (Fig. 49 (*a*)). Smoke particles observed through a high-powered microscope C appear to 'jiggle' or move haphazardly (Fig. 49 (*b*)).

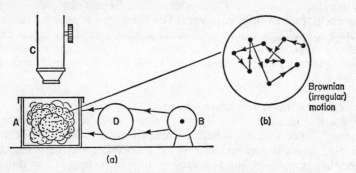

(*a*)

Fig. 49. Brownian motion in gas

*Explanation.* The number of molecules of the liquid or gas bombarding one side of the particle in all directions at any instant are never exactly equal to the number bombarding the opposite side at the same instant. When the particle is *very small*, the difference in these numbers of molecules is appreciable compared with their actual number. The fine particle hence moves in the direction of the resultant force. As soon as it reaches a new position the same thing happens again. The force is a random one in direction and magnitude because the molecules move randomly in all different directions and with different speeds.

For *large particles*, the difference in the number of particles bombarding opposite sides is not appreciable compared with the actual number. The resultant force is thus practically zero. A table-tennis ball in air would not move, even though it is bombarded on all sides by air molecules.

### Motion of Molecules

(i) *To demonstrate in liquids*, fill jar one-third with concentrated sugar solution, the next third with concentrated copper sulphate solution, using a pipette, and finally with layer of distilled water. At first, the boundaries and the liquids are distinct. After a time, water *and* sugar are both seen to be blue.

*Conclusion.* Molecules of copper sulphate move in all directions.

(ii) *Gases.* Fill a gas jar with the brown gas nitrogen peroxide and seal it with a cover slip. Then place an inverted empty jar of air on top. Remove the cover slip quickly. After a short time there is a uniform brown colour in both jars.

*Conclusion.* Molecules of gases move in different directions.

### Numbers of Molecules

To demonstrate the enormously large numbers of molecules present in a small mass, dissolve 1 gram of fluorescein in a litre of water and observe the green colour due to fluorescein molecules. Remove 1 c.c. by pipette, dilute it to 1 litre with water. Repeat this dilution and observe if a green tinge is present. The third litre of solution contains $1/1000 \times 1/1000 \times 1/1000$ or $1/10^9$ of the number of molecules originally present in 1 gram of fluorescein. Thus there are at least $10^9$ (thousand million) molecules in this small mass if the green colour is present.

### Oil Film and Molecular Diameter

Count the number of oil drops obtained from a 1 cm³ pipette or syringe; hence find the volume of one drop. Or, collect one drop of olive-oil on a fine wire and observe the diameter by viewing it against a $\frac{1}{2}$-millimetre scale—volume of drop $= 4\pi r^3/3$. (A drop of liquid detergent, in place of oil, is very suitable.)

Using lycopodium powder, lightly dust the surface of clean water in a very large clean shallow and levelled vessel L (Fig. 50). Allow an oil drop to fall in the centre of the water. Quickly measure the maximum diameter of the oil film F which spreads out.

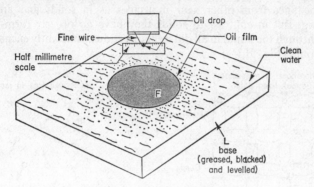

FIG. 50. Oil film experiment

*Calculation.* Suppose the oil drop has a volume of $1/100$ cm$^3$ and the film an approximate diameter of 20 cm or radius 10 cm. Then area of film $= \pi r^2 = \pi \times 10^2 = 300$ cm$^2$ (approx.),

$$\therefore \text{thickness of oil film} = \frac{\text{volume}}{\text{area}} = \frac{1}{100 \times 300} = 3 \times 10^{-5} \text{ cm (approx.)}$$

Accurate experiments with very clean water and a sufficiently large surface area show that a *monomolecular layer* is formed by a tiny drop of oil which spreads over the water. The oil molecule consists of a chain of about 18 carbon atoms, which stick out perpendicularly to the water surface. The film thickness divided by this number of atoms gives an average value for the diameter of a carbon atom, about $4 \times 10^{-8}$ cm.

### Molecules in Solids, Liquids, Gases

*Solids* are characterized by a rigid geometrical form. The molecules inside them have a constant mean or average position. They are kept there by strong attractive and repulsive forces or bonds between the molecules (Fig. 51 (*a*)).

But the molecules are restless; they *vibrate* about their mean position. Their maximum displacement during vibration, or *amplitude*, depends on the temperature of the solid. When it is heated, the amplitude increases. The temperature of the solid now rises—the molecules have greater energy than before. The specific heat capacity (p. 65) is equal to the increase in energy per gram per deg C temperature rise.

The increase in amplitude on heating accounts for the increase in length of the solid (thermal expansion). It also explains the conduction of heat along the metal (thermal conduction). See pp. 71, 84.

*Liquids* have no geometrical form; they can be poured into a vessel of any shape. On the average the molcules inside them are about the same distance from other near molecules as in solids and are also vibrating. But in contrast to solids they have no orderly form—they move through the liquid in all different directions, constantly exchanging neighbours (Fig. 51 (*b*)).

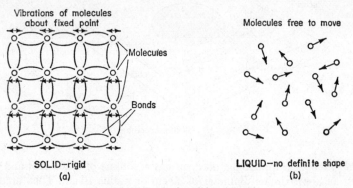

FIG. 51, Molecules in solid and liquid

When the liquid temperature rises, the mean speed of the molecules through the liquid, and their vibration, increase. As the temperature is lowered, the reverse happens.

*Gases*, like liquids, have no geometrical form; they fill completely any space whatever its shape or volume, whereas liquids have a constant volume.

Unlike solids and liquids, the force of attraction between the molecules of a gas in normal conditions is extremely small. The molecules hence move about swiftly in all different directions, that is, their motion is random, and lead an independent existence. When they collide with the walls of the containing vessel they produce an average 'gas pressure' (p. 43).

## FORCES IN SOLIDS AND LIQUIDS

*Solids*

*Elasticity.* *Experiment.* Suspend a spring S from a clamp, attach a scale-pan and a pointer P, place a vertical half-metre rule M beside S (Fig. 52 (*a*)). Add weights to the scale-pan, record the extension each time and the total load or tension *W*, up to a moderate load. Remove the weights and again record the extension. Repeat, this time adding weights until a very heavy load is reached and the spring is strained. Plot a graph of extension *v.* load for the two cases.

*Result.* (1) For a small load, a straight-line graph OL passing through the origin is obtained (Fig. 52 (*b*)). Thus the extension is directly proportional to tension or load. (2) For a heavy load, the graph is a straight line to L but it curves from L to M and the spring is permanently strained. L is the *elastic limit*; it is the load beyond which the extension is no longer proportional to the load.

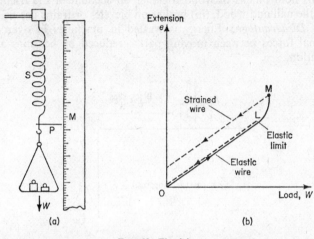

FIG. 52. Elasticity

Repeat the experiment with a long thin copper wire (26 s.w.g.), adding suitable loads and removing them, and observing the elasticity of the wire, the elastic limit, the yield point (the point when the wire becomes 'plastic'), and the breaking point of the wire.

*Conclusions.* (1) The extension of a spring is proportional to the tension or load, provided the elastic limit is not exceeded (*Hooke's law*).

(2) Beyond the elastic limit, the extension increases rapidly and the metal 'yields' and may break with increasing loads.

*Molecular Theory.* In the case of the spring, the weight at the end produced a change of *shape* in the metal. In the case of the straight wire, the weight applied produced a change of *length* in the metal. In either case elastic forces are obtained for moderate stresses in the wire; that is, up to the elastic limit, the forces between the displaced molecules restore them to their original position when the stress is removed.

Beyond the elastic limit there is permanent strain and the metal atoms or ions slide over each other to a new alignment of crystals which is much weaker, so that the metal breaks with increasing loads.

Note that elastic forces resist compression—the attractive forces between molecules increase as their distance apart decreases. But since solids (and liquids) cannot be compressed beyond a certain limit, the forces between the molecules when they are extremely close together are *repulsive*.

### Friction

*Advantages:* (i) Without friction we could not walk over surfaces, (ii) nails hold blocks of wood together on account of the friction between the nail and wood, (iii) brakes on bicycles or trains use frictional forces. *Disadvantage:* Energy is wasted in machines in overcoming frictional forces between moving parts—reduced by bearings and by lubrication.

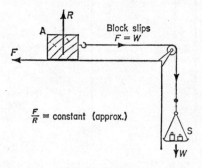

FIG. 53. Friction

*Experiment.* Place a block of wood A on a table or other surface, and connect it to a scale-pan S by a string passing over a grooved wheel (Fig. 53). Add weights to S until A is just on the point of slipping. Record the total weight $W$ due to the weights and S. This is equal to the *limiting frictional force* $F$, the maximum frictional force. Turn the block over so that a surface of different area is in contact with the table. Observe that the limiting frictional force is practically the same as before.

Increase the *normal reaction*, $R$, on the block by placing a weight on A. Find the new limiting frictional force $F$. Increase the magnitude of $R$ further and repeat the experiment.

*Results.* (i) The limiting frictional force $F$ is independent of the area in contact for a given normal reaction $R$, (ii) the ratio $F/R$ = constant, approximately.

*Laws of Solid Friction.* 1. Friction opposes motion. 2. The limiting frictional force, $F$, is independent of the area of the surfaces in contact for a given normal reaction between them. 3. The ratio $F/R$ = constant, approximately.

*Static and Kinetic (Dynamic) Friction.* When an object is on the point of slipping, for example, when a ladder is leaning against a wall, this is an example of 'static friction'. When one moving surface rubs against another surface, for example, when the metal rim of a wheel rubs against a brake block, the frictional force is 'kinetic or dynamic friction', $F'$. Experiment shows $F'/R =$ a constant, approximately, where $R$ is the normal reaction.

*Rolling Friction: Ball Bearings.* To reduce frictional forces, large blocks of stone have circular logs beneath them and can then be pulled more easily along the ground. The logs roll, thus reducing the relative velocity between surfaces in contact. *Ball-bearings* between the hub and axle of a bicycle wheel roll round the axle, reducing friction.

*Molecular Theory.* Friction between metal surfaces is caused by the 'welding' together of groups of molecules or atoms on their surfaces. The molecules and atoms concerned occupy only a small part of the geometrical area of the surfaces in contact, so the pressure on them is very high and welding occurs.

### Liquids
*Surface Tension.* Examples of surface tension forces are:
1. Hairs of a wet painting brush cling together—forces at edges of water film pull hairs together (Fig. 54 (a)).

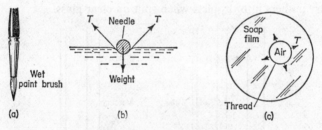

FIG. 54. Surface tension effects

2. Dry needle floats on water—forces, $T$, on 'skin' of liquid have an upward resultant which balances the weight (Fig. 54 (b)).
3. A closed light thread is pulled into a circle when placed on a soap film surface and the surface inside is pierced (Fig. 54 (c)). Surface tension forces, $T$, pull the thread out.

*Molecular Explanation.* A molecule X inside the liquid is attracted equally by molecules all round it inside the 'sphere of molecular attraction'. The resultant force is then zero (Fig. 55 (i)). A molecule Y on the surface has a resultant attractive force towards the interior of the liquid because there are relatively fewer molecules outside (Fig. 55 (ii)). The effect is to pull molecules towards the interior, so that the number of molecules in the surface, or surface area, is the minimum possible for the given volume of liquid. This makes (i) a surface in which forces

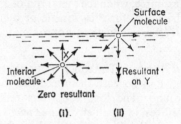

FIG. 55. Explanation of surface tension

called 'surface tension forces' act, (ii) liquids such as raindrops or small mercury drops practically spherical—a sphere is a shape which has the least surface area for a given volume. Large mercury drops are flattened at the top owing to gravitational attraction.

*Cohesion: Adhesion.* *Cohesion* is the name given to the forces of attraction between *like* molecules. *Adhesion* is the name given to the forces of attraction between *unlike* molecules. Water 'wets' clean glass because the force of adhesion between glass and water molecules is greater than that between water molecules. For an opposite reason, mercury gathers into droplets when spilt on clear glass.

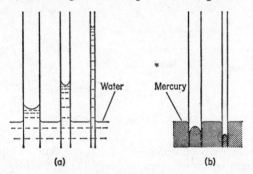

FIG. 56. Capillary rise and fall

*Capillarity.* Water rises in wet capillary (fine-bore) tubes—the smaller the radius, the greater is the height of the water (Fig. 56 (*a*)). The adhesion between molecules of glass and water is greater than between molecules of water. Mercury is depressed in capillary tubes, for an opposite reason (Fig. 56 (*b*)).

Ink rises up blotting paper, liquids rise up sugar cubes, and water rises from below ground to the roots of vegetables and plants, owing to capillarity in fine pores.

*Impurities.* Impurities lower the surface tension of pure water. Soap solution has a smaller surface tension than water. Pieces of camphor dart about in water; the surface tension decreases more on the side where it dissolves faster, so that a resultant force acts on the camphor continually. The movement ceases when the solution has a uniform concentration. For the same reason a drop of olive oil spreads over water (p. 55).

*Viscosity.* Viscosity is the name given to the frictional force exerted by a liquid. A small steel ball-bearing falls very quickly through a cylinder full of water or paraffin-oil, but very slowly through glycerine or syrup. The latter are therefore much more viscous.

In steady flow, called *uniform* or *laminar* flow, along a pipe, particles or layers of the liquid at the same distance from the axis have the same velocity. The velocity decreases from a maximum value at the centre or axis to zero at the walls of the tube, so that a *velocity gradient* exists across each layer.

*Law:* The frictional force acting on a layer of liquid moving along in uniform flow is proportional to the area of the layer and to the velocity gradient where it is situated.

Observe that (i) in solid friction the frictional force is independent of the area, but in fluid friction it is directly proportional to the area, (ii) in solid friction the frictional force between two surfaces in relative motion is practically independent of the relative velocity but in fluid friction it is directly proportional to the velocity gradient.

*Terminal Velocity.* When a small steel ball-bearing is gently released into a tall jar of glycerine along the axis, its weight, $W$, is greater than the upthrust, $U$, of the liquid ($W$ = volume × density of steel, $U$ = volume × density of glycerine). The ball-bearing therefore accelerates. Now the frictional force due to viscosity is proportional to the velocity. Hence the frictional force, $F$, increases. When

$$W - U = F$$

there is no resultant force on the ball-bearing. Hence there is no longer acceleration. Consequently the velocity reaches a constant maximum value called the *terminal velocity.*

Very viscous liquids, glycerine and treacle for example, can be compared in viscosity by measuring with a stop-watch the terminal velocity of a small steel ball-bearing in each liquid.

# 3 Heat

## THERMOMETRY

### Temperature Scales

All thermometer scales have two fixed temperatures on them: (i) *lower fixed point*—this is the temperature of pure melting ice and is often known as the 'ice point'. (ii) *Upper fixed point*—this is the temperature of steam above water boiling at a pressure of 76 cm mercury and is often known as the 'steam point'.

*Celsius (Centigrade) Scale.* The lower fixed point is called '0°C', the upper fixed point is '100°C', and hence the temperature interval between is 100 (100–0) degC (Fig. 57 (*a*)).

*Fahrenheit Scale.* The lower fixed point is called '32°F', the upper fixed point is '212°F'.

*Absolute or Thermodynamic Temperature Scale.* Temperature in SI units is measured on this scale. The lower fixed point is 0 K (kelvin degrees), called absolute zero. The upper fixed point is 273·16 K, the 'triple point' of water (the temperature when water, ice and water-vapour are in equilibrium). Approximately,

$$0°C = 273 \text{ K}, 100°C = 373 \text{ K}.$$

See p. 78. A temperature change of 1 degC = a change of 1 K. Thus the heat capacity of a metal block, for example, may be written either as 50 J/degC or as 60 J/K in SI units (see p. 65).

*Marking Fixed Points.* A *mercury-in-glass* thermometer is made by (i) choosing a uniform capillary tube—tested by measuring the length of a mercury thread at different parts, (ii) sealing one end and blowing a bulb here, (iii) filling the bulb with mercury by placing a funnel with the liquid on the open end and then warming and cooling the closed end repeatedly, (iv) finally boiling all the mercury to drive air out and sealing the top.

Fig. 57 (*b*) shows how the mercury level for the lower fixed point or *ice point* is obtained. Fig. 57 (*c*) shows how the upper fixed point or *steam point* is obtained. An inner jacket prevents radiation or cooling of the thermometer; and a water manometer M provides the actual steam pressure, so that a correction can be made to the figure of 100°C if this is not 76 cm mercury. Steady conditions are needed.

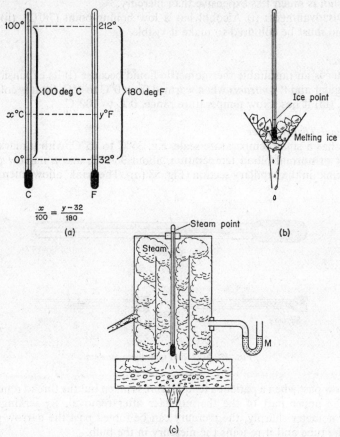

$$\frac{x}{100} = \frac{y-32}{180}$$

FIG. 57. Temperature

### Mercury-in-glass Thermometer

Advantages: (i) Fairly regular expansion of mercury, (ii) mercury does not 'wet' glass, (iii) mercury is visible and highly reflecting, (iv) fairly wide temperature range, 350°C to −40°C, (iv) mercury has high thermal conductivity compared to other liquids.

Disadvantages: (i) Mercury has not a low freezing point (−40°C) and the thermometer cannot be used in Arctic regions, (ii) mercury is expensive.

### Alcohol-in-glass Thermometer
Advantages: (i) Low freezing point (−112°C) and can hence be used in polar regions, (ii) alcohol has large expansion on heating, (iii) alcohol is much less expensive than mercury.

Disadvantages: (i) Alcohol has a low boiling-point (78°C), (ii) the liquid must be coloured to make it visible.

### Water
Water is an unsuitable thermometric liquid because (i) its expansion is irregular and it *contracts* when warmed from 0°C to 4°C, (ii) it is colourless, (iii) it has a low temperature range, 0°C to 100°C.

### Clinical Thermometer
This has a small temperature scale, e.g. 35°C to 45°C, with a marking on it of normal blood temperature, about 36·9°C, and a narrow part or 'kink' in the capillary section (Fig. 58 (a)). The 'kink' allows mercury

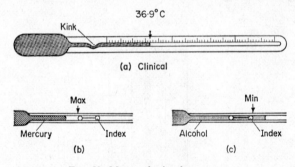

FIG. 58. Max. and min. thermometers

to flow past when a patient's temperature is taken but the thread remains in the upper part of the thermometer after removal. By jerking the thermometer sharply, the mercury can be forced past the narrow part of the tube and it re-joins the mercury in the bulb.

### Maximum Thermometers
These use mercury-in-glass. Mercury has a *convex* meniscus and hence pushes an index in front of it when the temperature rises. The maximum temperature corresponds to the lower end of the index (Fig. 58 (b)).

### Minimum Thermometers

These use alcohol-in-glass. Alcohol has a *concave* meniscus. An index in the alcohol is hence pulled down when the temperature falls, and remains in position when the temperature rises. The minimum temperature corresponds to the upper end of the index (Fig. 58 (c)).

## HEAT AND ENERGY MEASUREMENTS

### Heat

'Heat' is a form of *energy*; but 'temperature' is a property which determines whether heat will flow to or from a particular body with which it is placed in contact.

*Molecular Theory.* When heat is given to a solid, its molecules vibrate with greater amplitude about a particular mean position. The energy of vibration thus increases. When heat is given to a liquid or a gas, the molecules move about faster than before. Their kinetic energy thus increases.

*Units of Heat.* 1. The *joule* (J) is the SI unit of heat since the joule is a unit of energy (p. 22).
   2. The *megajoule* (MJ) $= 10^6$ J $= 1000$ kJ.

*Definitions.* The *heat capacity* of a substance is the heat required to raise its temperature by 1 degC or 1 K. Unit: J/degC or J/K (p. 62).

The *calorific value* of food (or fuel) is the amount of heat per unit mass produced when it is eaten (or burned).

The *specific heat capacity* (c) of a substance is the heat required to raise the temperature of unit mass by 1 degC. Thus *specific heat capacity* is the *heat capacity per unit mass*. Unit: J per kg per K (J/kg K) or J per g per K (J/g K). The specific heat capacity of water $= 4200$J/ Kg K or 4·2 J/g K (approx.).
From above,

1. heat capacity = mass $\times$ specific heat capacity = $mc$,
2. heat gained or lost, $Q = mct$,

where $m$ is the mass of the object concerned, $c$ its specific heat capacity, and $t$ its temperature *change*.

*Examples.* 1. 200 g of water is heated from 15°C to 40°C. Calculate the heat supplied.

$$Q = mct = 200 \times 4·2 \times (40 - 15) = 21,000 \text{ J}$$

**2.** A metal block, mass 2 kg, is heated electrically by a 100 W heating coil for 5 min. The temperature of the block rises from 20°C to 30°C. Calculate the specific heat capacity of the metal.

Heat supplied, $Q = 100(W) \times 300(s) = 30,000$ J
From $Q = mct$,

$$c = \frac{Q}{mt} = \frac{30\ 000}{2 \times (30 - 20)}$$

$$= 1500 \text{ J/kg K}$$

### Mechanical Energy change to Heat Energy

**1.** *Gravitational Energy Change.* Invert a long tube containing lead shot many times, so that mechanical energy, due to gravity, is repeatedly changed into heat. Measure the final temperature rise.

*Calculation.* Suppose the height through which the lead drops each time is 1·5 metre, the number of drops is 80, and the final temperature rise is 8 degC. Then mechanical energy lost, if $m$ is the mass of lead in kg,

$= \text{weight} \times \text{height} = m \times 9 \cdot 8 \times 1 \cdot 5 \times 80 = 1176\ m$ joule.

Assuming all the energy is changed to heat, then heat to raise the temperature of 1 kg of lead by 1 degC = specific heat capacity,

$$= \frac{1176\ m}{m \times 8} = 150 \text{ J/kg K (approx.)}$$

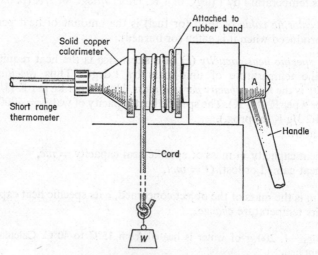

FIG. 59. Mechanical to heat energy

2. *Heat due to Friction.* A more accurate way of measuring mechanical energy change and the heat produced is to rotate a solid copper calorimeter against an opposing frictional force in a nylon cord wound round it, and then to measure the temperature rise produced (Fig. 59). In the experiment, the crank A is turned at such a rate that the rubber band, to which the other nylon end is attached, becomes slack. The work done is then *only* against the frictional force equal to the weight $W$ at the end of the cord.

*Calculation.* Suppose the weight $W$ is 50 N, the calorimeter is turned 200 times, the diameter of the drum is 2·54 cm, its mass is 190 g or 0·19 kg, and its temperature rise is 10 degC. Then

mechanical energy spent

$$= \text{force in newtons} \times \text{distance in metres}$$
$$= 50 \times \pi \times (2·54/100) \times 200$$
$$= 800 \text{ J}$$

Heat produced $= 0·19 \times c \times 10$

where $c$ is the sp. ht. capacity of copper in J/kg K. Assuming all the work done is converted into heat which raises the temperature of the calorimeter, heat produced $= 800$ J.

$$\therefore c = \frac{800}{0·19 \times 10} = 420 \text{ J/kg K}$$

### Heat Measurements

Heat capacity, calorific value, specific heat capacity and burner temperatures may be measured by the method of mixtures. To minimise heat losses to the surroundings, (i) the calorimeter used is well-lagged to reduce conduction and well-polished to reduce radiation, (ii) the temperature rise of the water in the calorimeter must not be too high; otherwise heat is lost by evaporation of water and by cooling.

(1) *Heat Capacity of Solid.* Heat the solid to a temperature such as 100°C in boiling water, and quickly transfer to cold water in a calorimeter.

*Calculation.* Suppose the water has a mass of 60 g and $c = 4200$ J/kg K for water, the calorimeter has mass of 80 g and $c = 400$ J/kg K, and the water temperature rises from 15°C to 21°C. Then, with mass in kg,

heat lost by solid $= $ heat capacity $\times (100 - 21)$ J

and heat gained by water and calorimeter

$$= 0·060 \times 4200 \times (21 - 15) + 0·080 \times 400 \times (21 - 15) \text{ J}$$
$$= 60 \times 4·2 \times (21 - 15) + 80 \times 0·4 \times (21 - 15) \text{ J}$$
$$\therefore 79 \times \text{heat capacity} = 1512 + 192 = 1704$$
$$\therefore \text{heat capacity} = 21·6 \text{ J/K}$$

3

(2) *Calorific Value.*    Burn the finely-divided fuel or food in a crucible by an electrical heating coil, using oxygen for complete combustion (Fig. 60). The heat produced $Q$ is obtained from the temperature rise of the large calorimeter surrounding the fuel calorimeter, or heat = (heat capacity of water + heat capacity of calorimeter) × temperature rise. From the mass of fuel used, the *heat per kilogramme* can be calculated.

(3) *Specific Heat Capacity of Metal.*    As in (1) above, but in the calculation replace 'heat capacity' by 'mass of solid (known) × specific heat capacity'.

(4) *Specific Heat Capacity of Liquid.*    Use a metal of known specific heat capacity with which the liquid does not react, heat it to 100°C, and transfer quickly to the liquid in the calorimeter.

*Calculation.*    Suppose the metal has a mass of 20 g, $c = 800$ J/kg K, the mass of the calorimeter is 90 g, $c = 400$ J/kg K, and the mass of liquid, 50 g, rises in temperature from 16°C to 24°C. Then, with mass in kg,

heat gained by liquid and calorimeter

$$= 0{\cdot}050 \times (24 - 16) + 0{\cdot}090 \times 400 \times (24 - 16) \text{ joule}$$

and    heat lost by metal $= 0{\cdot}020 \times 800 \times (100 - 24)$ joule

$$\therefore\ 0{\cdot}4c + 288 = 1216$$

$$\therefore\ c = 2300 \text{ J/kg K}$$

(5) *Burner Temperature.*    Place a hot metal in the burner, then transfer it quickly to water in a calorimeter and observe the temperature rise.

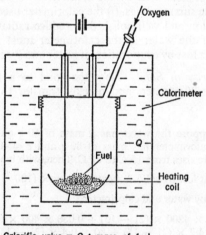

Calorific value = $Q$ ÷ mass of fuel

Fig. 60. Fuel calorimeter

*Calculation.* Suppose the mass of metal is 30 g, $c = 800$ J/kg K and initial (burner) temperature is $x°$C. If the mass of water is 80 g, mass of calorimeter is 120 g, $c = 400$ J/kg K, and water temperature rises from 12°C to 40°C, then, with mass in kg,

$$\text{heat lost by metal} = 0.030 \times 800 \times (x - 40)$$

and using $c = 4200$ J/kg K for water,

$$\text{heat gained by water and calorimeter}$$
$$= 0.080 \times 4200 \times (40 - 12) + 0.120 \times 400 \times (40 - 12)$$
$$\therefore \quad 24x - 960 = 10{,}752 \quad \text{or} \quad x = 488°C \text{ (approx.).}$$

# LATENT HEAT

### Fusion (Solid to liquid state)
When heat is supplied continuously to a solid, the amplitude of vibration of the molecules increases more and more. Eventually, the increased energy of the molecules enables them to break free from the molecular bonds which kept them in 'anchored' mean positions. They now move about freely and form the liquid state. A solid thus begins to melt or 'fuse' if heated sufficiently.

### Vaporisation (Liquid to gaseous state)
The molecules inside a liquid move about at different speeds, constantly exchanging neighbours. When the liquid is heated, the energy of the molecules increases. At one stage, *all* the molecules gain sufficient energy to break the bonds which keep them in the liquid state. The liquid thus begins to 'boil'.

### Definitions
1. *Specific latent heat of vaporisation* ($l$) is the heat required to change unit mass of a liquid at the boiling-point to vapour or gas at the same temperature.

2. *Specific latent heat of fusion* ($l$) is the heat required to change unit mass of a solid at the melting-point to liquid at the same temperature.

*Experiments.* 1. *Specific latent heat of steam (or vaporisation of water).* Note that (i) a steam- or water-trap P is essential so that dry steam passes into the calorimeter (Fig. 61), (ii) pass steam until the temperature rise is about 15 deg C—a higher temperature than 35°C produces evaporation of water which may lead to error, (iii) the mass of steam is found by weighing the calorimeter and water before and after.

*Calculation.* Suppose 2.0 g of steam is passed, the temperature of the water rises from 15°C to 27°C, the mass of water is 90 g, $c = 4200$ J/kg K, and the mass of calorimeter is 80 g, $c = 400$ J/kg. Then, with mass in kg,

$$\text{heat given up by steam} = 0.002l + 0.002 \times 4200 \times (100 - 27)$$
$$= 0.002l + 613 \text{ joule.}$$

and

    heat gained by water and calorimeter

$$= 0 \cdot 090 \times 4200 \times (27 - 15) + 0 \cdot 080 \times 400 (27 - 15) = 4920 \text{ J}$$
$$\therefore 0 \cdot 002l + 613 = 4920$$
$$l = 2 \cdot 15 \times 10^6 \text{ J/kg}$$

2. *Specific latent heat of ice.* Note that (i) the ice *must* be dried with blotting or filter paper before being added to water in the calorimeter, (ii) small pieces of dry ice are better to use than a large piece to control the temperature fall and to ensure the ice temperature is 0°C, (iii) the ice must all be melted before the final temperature is taken, (iv) the

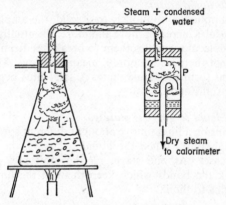

Fɪɢ. 61. Latent heat of vaporisation

final temperature should not be too low otherwise water vapour from the air will condense on the water. A good practical point is to warm the water first by 4 degrees, for example, above the surroundings temperature and then to cool it with ice until its temperature drops 4 degrees below that of the surroundings. This method compensates for heat gained from the surroundings by the water on cooling, which would otherwise introduce an error.

*Calculation.* Suppose 2·5 g of ice cools 30 g of water from 18°C to 12°C after melting and the calorimeter has a mass of 100 g, $c = 400$ J/kg K = 0·4 J/g K. Then, with $l$ in J/g,

    heat gained by ice $= 2 \cdot 5l + 2 \cdot 5 \times 4 \cdot 2 \times (12 - 0) = 2 \cdot 5l + 126$ joule

and

    heat lost by water and calorimeter

$$= 30 \times 4 \cdot 2 \times (18 - 12) + 100 \times 0 \cdot 4 \times (18 - 12) = 996 \text{ joule}$$
$$\therefore 2 \cdot 5l + 126 = 996 \quad \text{or} \quad l = 348 \text{ J/g}$$

*Melting Point*

For a pure substance like naphthalene, fill a test-tube A, melt *all* the solid by using a beaker and hot water, and then remove A and allow it to cool. With the aid of a thermometer, observe the temperature at equal intervals of time. Plot a cooling (temperature *v.* time) graph. The *flat part* corresponds to the melting point. Reason: When the naphthalene begins to solidify, the latent heat given up balances the heat lost to the surroundings. The temperature thus remains constant.

A very thin wire wound round a large ice block, with heavy weights at each end of the wire, gradually sinks into and through the ice (regelation). The melting point of ice is lowered by pressure; so the ice below the wire melts and freezes again round the upper side where the pressure is less.

## EXPANSION OF SOLIDS AND LIQUIDS

*Expansion of Solids*

Solids such as metals expand when heated. On kinetic theory, the amplitude of vibration of the molecules increases, so their average distance apart increases (see p. 56).

A *bimetal bar*, having equal lengths of brass and iron riveted together, curves when heated, with brass on the outside (Fig. 62). Thus brass expands more than iron over the same temperature range. Cooling over equal temperature ranges produces a greater decrease in length in brass—the strip now curves the other way.

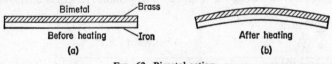

Bimetal          Brass

Before heating   Iron              After heating
(a)                                (b)

FIG. 62. Bimetal action

*Applications of Bimetal Strips.*  1. *Balance-wheel of watch*—the rim is made of two different metals, with the more expansible metal on the outside, and balance-weights are distributed round the rim. When the temperature rises the spring becomes less elastic and the radial arms of the wheel expands; but the rim curves round nearer to the centre of oscillation and compensates for both effects.

2. *Fire-alarm or thermostat.* In one form of fire-alarm a bimetal curls towards contacts on warming and makes an electrical circuit. In a thermostat it curls away from contacts and breaks the electrical circuit, as soon as a particular temperature is reached.

*Forces During Expansion and Contraction.*  A cast-iron pin at one end breaks if a metal bar is prevented from expansion or contraction.

A large force is therefore exerted when metals rise or fall in temperature and are fixed at both ends. Thus (i) telegraph wires are allowed to sag when fixed in summer-time—allowance is then made for contraction in winter, (ii) railway lines over open country are laid in sections with a *small gap* between them to allow for expansion.

*Linear expansivity of solid.*   Definition: This is the increase in length per unit length per degC temperature rise. Alternatively,

$$\text{expansivity, } \alpha = \frac{\text{increase in length}}{\text{original length} \times \text{temp. rise}}$$

Units: 'per degC' or 'per K'—the units of length cancel in numerator and denominator.

Thus if the linear expansivity, $\alpha$, of steel is 0·000012 per K, then 1 cm (or 1 metre) of steel expands by 0·000012 cm (or 0·000012 metre) for 1 degC temperature rise. Hence 50 cm of steel, heated for a 30 degC temperature rise, expands by 0·000012 × 50 × 30 or 0·018 cm. Note that, if $\alpha$ = linear expansivity, $l$ = original length, $t$ = temperature *change*, then

$$\text{increase in length} = \alpha l t \qquad \qquad \ldots(1)$$

$$\therefore \text{ new length, } l_t = l + \alpha l t = l(1 + \alpha t) \qquad \ldots(2)$$

*Experiment to Measure Linear Expansivity.*   In one form of apparatus, the bar AB is surrounded by a lagged jacket, steam is passed to heat up all the bar, and one end A of the bar is fixed so that expansion takes place *only* at the free end B (Fig. 63). The original length is measured by

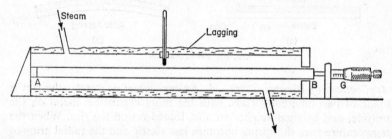

FIG. 63. Measurement of linear expansivity

a metre rule because an error of a millimetre (0·1 cm) in a bar length such as 80·0 cm is only a very small percentage error. The increase in length, such as 1 or 2 millimetres, is so small that a metre rule is useless and a micrometer screw gauge G must be used. The constancy of the gauge reading will show if all the rod has reached its final temperature and expansion is complete.

*Calculation.* Suppose the original length of the bar is 101·5 cm, the initial and final temperatures are 15°C and 100°C, respectively, and the increase in length is 1·40 mm or 0·14 cm. Then

$$\text{linear expansivity, } \alpha = \frac{0·14 \text{ cm}}{101·5 \text{ cm} \times 85 \text{ K}}$$

$$= 0·000016 \, (16 \times 10^{-6})/\text{K}$$

Note that, since $\alpha$ is not a constant, it is better to describe the result as the 'mean (average) linear coefficient in the temperature range 15°C to 100°C'.

*Area (Superficial) Expansivity.* The surface area expansivity, $\beta$, of a metal is the increase in area per unit area per degC temperature rise. Calculation shows that $\beta = 2\alpha$.

*Cubic Expansivity.* The cubic expansivity, $\gamma$, of a metal is the increase in volume per unit volume per degC temperature rise. Calculation shows that $\gamma = 3\alpha$.

## Expansion of Liquids

Liquids expand about ten times as much as solids for the same temperature change. They expand only in *volume*, i.e. we deal only with cubic expansion, whereas solids can expand in length or area (e.g. the roof of a metal shed) or volume (e.g. the volume of a solid block).

When liquids are heated the material of the container also expands. We therefore distinguish between the 'absolute or true expansivity' (which takes the container material expansion into account) and the 'apparent expansivity' (which ignores the expansion of the container).

Definitions: 1. The *apparent expansivity* is the increase in volume relative to that of the vessel per unit volume per degC rise.

2. The *absolute (true) expansivity*, $\gamma$, is the increase in volume per unit volume per degC rise. Or,

$$\gamma = \frac{\text{increase in volume}}{\text{original volume} \times \text{temp. rise}}$$

Thus if the original volume of a liquid is 100·0 cm³, the temperature rises from 15°C to 65°C and the increase in volume is 2·0 cm³, then

$$\gamma = \frac{2·0 \text{ cm}^3}{100·0 \text{ cm}^3 \times 50 \text{ K}} = 0·0004/\text{K}$$

Note that (i) the units of $\gamma$ are 'per K' since the volume unit cancels in numerator and denominator, (ii) the result for $\gamma$ should be described as the '*mean* cubic expansivity in the temperature range 15°C–65°C', since $\gamma$ is not a constant.

*Relation.*

> *Absolute (true) expansivity = apparent expansivity + g*

where $g$ is the cubic expansivity (3 × linear expansivity) of the material of the vessel. Thus if apparent expansivity from experiment is 0·00024 /K and $c$ is 0·00001/K for the glass material, then the absolute expansivity is 0·00025/K. Silica expands so slightly that $g$ is negligibly small for this material.

*Measurement of Apparent Expansivity.* This can be done with (i) a dilatometer—a glass bottle fitted with a stopper having a long fine uniform bore tube G with graduations (Fig. 64 (*a*)), or (ii) a 1-litre flask with an inverted small pipette (e.g. 2 cm³) in the stopper (Fig. 64 (*b*)).

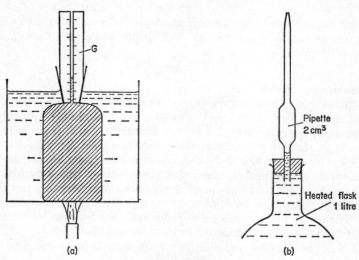

(a)                                        (b)

FIG. 64. Cubic expansion of liquid

With a *dilatometer*, the volume expansion is measured on the fine bore tube. The apparent expansivity can then be calculated from 'increase in volume/(original volume × temp. rise)'. The liquid in the *flask*, however, is warmed gently until it just fills the whole of the pipette, and the particular temperature is then observed. The apparent coefficient can then be calculated. Note that the dilatometer method would give more reliable results because the whole volume of the liquid is here kept at the same temperature by surrounding it with water in the beaker. In the flask method, however, some parts of the liquid are not at the same temperature as others.

*Formulae.* Since $\gamma$ is the increase in volume of 1 cm³ when warmed through 1 degC, it follows that, for a volume of $V$ cm³ and a temperature rise of $t$ degC,

$$\text{increase in volume} = \gamma V t \qquad \ldots (1)$$

$$\therefore \text{ new volume, } V_t = V + \gamma V t = V(1 + \gamma t) \qquad \ldots (2)$$

*Example.* The bulb of a mercury thermometer up to the 0°C mark has a volume of 0·5 cm³. Calculate the volume of the capillary tube between the 0°C and 100°C divisions, given the true expansivity of mercury is $18 \times 10^{-5}$ (0·00018)/K and the cubic expansivity of the glass is $1 \times 10^{-5}$/K.

Apparent expansivity $= 18 \times 10^{-5} - 1 \times 10^{-5} = 17 \times 10^{-5}$/K

$\therefore$ increase in volume from 0°C to 100°C

$$= \text{apparent expansivity} \times \text{volume} \times \text{temp. rise}$$
$$= 17 \times 10^{-5} \times 0\cdot5 \times 100 = 8\cdot5 \times 10^{-3} \text{ cm}^3$$
$$= \text{volume of capillary}$$

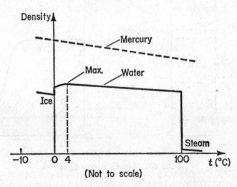

FIG. 65. Density of water and mercury

*Density Changes.* A solid expands slightly with temperature rise. Consequently its density (mass/volume) decreases slightly. An equal volume of liquid expands much more than a solid for the same temperature rise. Thus its density decreases much more.

Most liquids expand when their temperature rises from 0°C to 100°C. Water is an exception. The density variation is compared with mercury in Fig. 65, which behaves in a regular way between 0°C and 100°C. Starting with the solid state, *ice* at −10°C expands when warmed to 0°C, but then *contracts on melting* while its temperature remains at 0°C. Hope's experiment (see later) shows that *water decreases in volume when warmed from 0°C to about 4°C*. After 4°C it behaves normally and expands. At 100°C it changes into *steam* with an increase of about 1600 times its original volume.

Thus the density of water is a maximum at about 4°C (Fig. 65). In Arctic regions, as the temperature of the top of a lake drops from 8°C, for example, the water here first contracts and sinks to the bottom, since it becomes denser. When the water temperature at the bottom reaches 4°C, however, the water above does not sink any lower as its temperature falls to 0°C. Below 0°C, ice forms on the surface and *thickens downwards*. But the water at the bottom remains at 4°C.

*Hope's experiment.* A tall jar A is filled with water and the middle is surrounded by a freezing mixture, F (Fig. 66 (*a*)). Thermometers P, Q record temperatures at the top and bottom of the water. The lowest recorded temperature at the bottom is about 4°C. Water at first sinks to the bottom from the middle as the temperature here is lowered (curve B); but after the whole of the water below F reaches 4°C, the water rises and the temperature at the top becomes lowered (curve E) (Fig. 66 (*b*)).

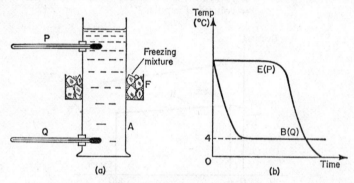

Fig. 66. Hope's experiment

# EXPANSION OF GASES

Gases expand much more than liquids. Unlike solids and liquids, they are sensitive to pressure changes. Always take into account both the pressure and the volume changes when the temperature of a gas varies.

*Cubic Expansivity (Volume Coefficient).* Definition: This is the increase in volume per unit volume at 0°C per degC temperature rise, the pressure and mass of gas being constant. Alternatively, with constant mass and pressure,

$$\text{cubic expansivity} = \frac{\text{increase in volume from } 0°C}{\text{volume at } 0°C \times \text{temp. rise}}$$

Note carefully that the initial volume of the gas *must be at* 0°C. This is the standard initial temperature for determining gas expansivities.

Further, the pressure must be kept constant while the volume changes, as shown below.

From the definition, if $\alpha$ is the cubic expansivity, $v_0$ is the gas volume at 0°C and $v_t$ is the increased volume at $t$°C, then

$$\alpha = \frac{v_t - v_0}{v_0 \times t}$$

*Measurement of Cubic Expansivity.* A simple laboratory method is to trap a column of air inside a wide-bore uniform capillary tube S closed at one end by a mercury (or sulphuric acid) thread, M (Fig. 67 (a)). A metre rule R enables the length $l$ of the air column, which is proportional to the volume, $v$, to be read. The temperature of the air can be varied by adding warm water to G. Readings of volume, $v$, with temperature, $t$, are taken. *The volume of the air is always at constant pressure*, which is equal to atmospheric pressure plus the length of the mercury thread.

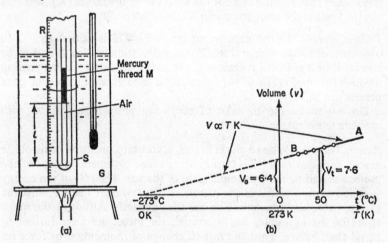

FIG. 67. Cubic Expansivity (Volume coefficient) of gas

In more elaborate and accurate apparatus, the gas pressure is kept constant by equalising levels of mercury before the volume readings are taken. One level is on the trapped gas side, the other is open to the atmosphere, in which case the pressure of the gas is always equal to atmospheric pressure.

*Calculation.* Plot a graph of volume (length), $v$, against temperature, $t$°C (Fig. 67 (b)). Find the volume at 0°C, $v_0$, by producing the straight-line AB to meet the volume axis. Suppose this is 6·4 cm. Take any other temperature such as 50°C, and read the volume here; suppose it is 7·6 cm. Then

$$\text{cubic expansivity, } \alpha = \frac{7\cdot6 - 6\cdot4}{6\cdot4 \times 50} = 0\cdot0038/\text{K}$$

*Absolute Temperature.*   Accurate experiments show that for permanent gases, $\alpha = 1/273$ per K (approx.). Thus 1 cm³ of the gas at 0°C would decrease to 262/273 cm³ at −1°C and *theoretically* to zero at −273°C (approx.). The *absolute zero* is the temperature at which the volume of a gas would theoretically be zero; it is about −273°C. In practice, gases liquefy before reaching this temperature.

*Absolute temperature,* expressed in degrees Kelvin (K), is the temperature reckoned from the absolute zero. Thus 0°C = 273K, 100°C = 373K. Generally,

$$T\,\text{K} = t(^\circ\text{C}) + 273$$

Remember that *T* is the symbol for absolute temperature (K), whereas *t* is the symbol for temperature in °C. See also p. 62.

*Volume and T.*   In the experiment on p. 77, 273 is added to $t$°C to obtain the absolute temperature, *T*. On calculation, $v/T$ is found to be constant; or a graph of *v* against *T* is found to be a straight line passing through the origin (Fig. 67 (*b*)). Thus, for a fixed mass of gas at constant pressure, $v \propto T$.

Do *not* make the mistake of confusing temperature in °C with *absolute* temperature.

*Kinetic Theory.*   When a gas is heated at constant pressure, some of the energy supplied raises the translational speed or kinetic energy of the molecules and hence the temperature of the gas. The rest of the energy supplied is used to move the piston of the container back against the external constant pressure. The gas thus expands. Although the mean speed of the molecules has increased, the molecules have further to travel than before. Thus the rate of change of momentum or force on the piston is the same as before, that is, the pressure is the same; but the volume has increased and the temperature has increased.

*Example.*   A gas has a volume of 40 cm³ at 15°C. (i) Find the new temperature if the volume is doubled, (ii) find the new volume if the temperature rises to 100°C, the pressure being constant in each case.

(i) Here $v_1 = 40$ cm³, $T_1 = 273 + 15 = 288$ K, and

$$\text{new volume, } v_2 = 80 \text{ cm}^3, T_2 = ?$$

From $v \propto T$, $v_1/v_2 = T_1/T_2$,

$$\therefore \frac{40}{80} = \frac{288}{T_2}$$

$$\therefore T_2 = 288 \times \frac{80}{40} = 576 \text{ K}$$

$$\therefore \text{ temperature in } °C = 576 - 273 = 303°C$$

(ii) Here $v_1 = 40 \text{ cm}^3$, $T_1 = 273 + 15 = 288$K,

$$v_2 = ?, T_2 = 273 + 100 = 373 \text{ K}$$

From $v \propto T$, $v_1/v_2 = T_1/T_2$,

$$\therefore \frac{40}{v_2} = \frac{288}{373}$$

$$\therefore v_2 = 40 \times \frac{373}{288} = 52 \text{ cm}^3$$

*Pressure Coefficient.* Now consider the *pressure* of a gas when the temperature changes, keeping the volume constant.

Definition: The *pressure coefficient* is the fractional increase in the pressure at 0°C for 1 degC temperature rise, the volume and mass of gas being constant. Or,

$$\text{pressure coefficient} = \frac{\text{increase in pressure from } 0°C}{\text{pressure at } 0°C \times \text{temp. rise}}$$

Note carefully that initially the pressure *must* be at 0°C.

From the definition, if $\alpha$ is the pressure coefficient, $p_0$ is the pressure at 0°C and $p_t$ is the increased pressure at $t$°C, then

$$\alpha = \frac{p_t - p_0}{p_0 \times t}$$

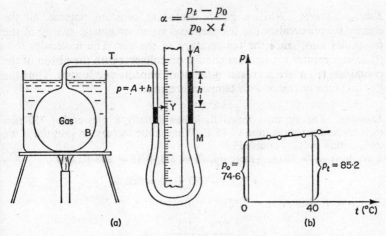

Fig. 68. Pressure coefficient of gas

*Measurement of Pressure Coefficient.* A large bulb, B, is used to contain the gas, air for example, and the pressure is measured with a mercury manometer, M (Fig. 68 (a)). *The volume of gas is kept constant by* raising the side M of the manometer until the mercury always reaches the index mark Y. This is done before pressure readings are taken as the temperature is varied. Note that a narrow tube T should be used for joining the manometer to B; the gas in this tube is not heated, but the error is reduced if its volume is made small relative to that of B.

*Calculation.* Take five values of pressure, $p$, at five different temperatures, $t$°C. (Pressure, $p$ = atmospheric pressure ± difference in levels.) Plot a graph of $p$ against $t$°C (Fig. 67 (b)). Draw the best straight line through all the points and produce it to cut the pressure-axis so that $p_0$ at 0°C is found. Suppose $p_0$ = 74·6 cm mercury.

Now take any other pressure, $p_t$. Suppose it is 85·2 cm mercury at 40°C. Then

$$\alpha = \frac{85 \cdot 2 - 74 \cdot 6}{74 \cdot 6 \times 40} = \frac{1}{280} \text{ /K (approx.)}$$

*Pressure Law.* The pressure coefficient of permanent gases is also accurately 1/273 per K, the same value as the volume coefficient. Thus

$$p \propto T \text{ (volume constant)}$$

where $T$ is the *absolute* temperature.

*Kinetic Theory.* When a gas is heated at constant volume, all the energy supplied raises the translational speed or kinetic energy of the molecules and hence the temperature of the gas. The molecules now (i) have a greater momentum change on collision with the piston of the container, (ii) make a greater number of impacts per second. Thus the gas pressure increases with temperature rise.

*Example.* The air in a sealed flask has initially a pressure of 750 mm mercury and a temperature of 15°C. What is the increase in pressure if the temperature in °C is doubled?

We have $p_1$ = 750 mm mercury, $T_1$ = 273 + 15 = 288 K, and

$$p_2 = ?, \ T_2 = 273 + 30 = 303 \text{ K}$$

Since $p \propto T$, then $p_1/p_2 = T_1/T_2$,

$$\therefore \frac{750}{p_2} = \frac{288}{303}$$

$$\therefore p_2 = 750 \times \frac{303}{288} = 790 \text{ mm mercury}$$

$$\therefore \text{ pressure increase} = 790 - 750 = 40 \text{ mm mercury}$$

### General Gas Law

From $v \propto T$ (pressure constant) and $p \propto T$ (volume constant), it follows that $pV \propto T$,

$$\therefore \frac{pV}{T} = \text{constant (fixed mass of gas)}$$

Thus if a fixed mass of gas has pressure, volume and *absolute* temperature values of, respectively, $p_1$, $V_1$, $T_1$ and $p_2$, $V_2$, $T_2$, then

$$\frac{p_1 V_1}{T_1} = \frac{p_2 V_2}{T_2}$$

*Reduction of Volume to S.T.P.* For comparing volumes of gases, the volumes collected in an experiment are often 'reduced' to *standard temperature and pressure* or S.T.P. This is 0°C and 760 mm mercury pressure.

*Example.* Reduce a volume of hydrogen of 120 cm³ at 20°C and 750 mm mercury pressure to S.T.P. Find the mass of hydrogen if its density is 0·09 g per litre at S.T.P.

We have $V_1 = 120$ cm³, $p_1 = 750$ mm mercury, $T_1 = 273 + 20 = 293$ K,

and $\qquad\qquad V_2 = ?$, $p_2 = 760$ mm mercury, $T_2 = 273$ K

From $p_1 V_1 / T_1 = p_2 V_2 / T_2$,

$$\therefore \frac{750 \times 120}{293} = \frac{760 \times V_2}{273}$$

$$\therefore V_2 = \frac{120 \times 750 \times 273}{760 \times 293} = 110 \text{ cm}^3 \text{ (approx.)}$$

$$\therefore \text{mass} = 110 \times 0\cdot00009 = 0\cdot01 \text{ g (approx.)}$$

## VAPOURS, VAPOUR PRESSURE, HUMIDITY

### Evaporation: Boiling

*Evaporation.* This is the change from liquid to vapour at a temperature below the normal boiling-point.

*Boiling.* This is the change from liquid to vapour when the saturation vapour pressure is equal to the external atmospheric pressure. In the former case the vapour is not in equilibrium with the liquid, whereas in boiling it is in equilibrium (see p. 69). Note that:

1. Evaporation takes place at all temperatures and occurs from the liquid surface. It increases with surface area, wind, lower relative humidity and higher liquid temperature.

2. Boiling occurs only at a fixed temperature for a given external atmospheric pressure, it takes place throughout the whole volume of liquid, and is independent of surface area or wind or relative humidity.

*Cooling Due to Evaporation.* (i) Liquid ether cools the hand as it evaporates. (ii) Place a beaker with liquid ether on top of some water on a wooden block (Fig. 69 (*a*)). Blow air through the ether to assist rapid evaporation. After a time the water changes to ice and the block has stuck to the wood.

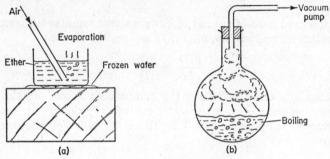

Fig. 69. Evaporation and boiling

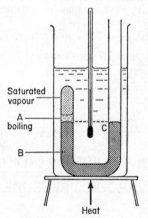

Fig. 70. Boiling point

*Kinetic Theory.* The molecules inside a liquid all move at different speeds. A few near the surface which are moving upwards very fast escape outside and become molecules of vapour or gas. This is 'evaporation'. The remainder of the liquid molecules then have a *smaller* average kinetic energy. Thus a liquid cools on evaporation. A wind removes molecules immediately outside the liquid, so that others near the surface can escape more quickly.

*Boiling Under Reduced Pressure.* Connect the top of a round-bottomed flask partly filled with water to a speedy pump (Fig. 69 (*b*)). Switch on the pump. In a short time the water begins to boil, even though no flame is used.

Explanation: Water boils when its saturation vapour pressure is equal to the external pressure. The pump reduces the air pressure outside the water to a value equal to the saturation vapour of water at room temperature (12·8 mm mercury at 15°C). The water then boils at room temperature.

*Boiling-point of Small Quantity of Liquid.* Confine a little of the liquid A on one side of a J-tube C by means of mercury, B (Fig. 70). Arrange the liquid level on the side C to be initially lower than at A by removing mercury if necessary. Place the J-tube in a tall beaker with water, heat slowly, and observe the temperature when the levels of mercury are the *same* on both sides. This is the boiling-point, since the saturation vapour pressure of the liquid is then equal to the external pressure.

*Measurement of S.V.P.* An 'unsaturated vapour' is one not in equilibrium with its liquid (p. 69). A 'saturated vapour' is one in equilibrium with its liquid. Unlike the unsaturated vapour, which obeys Boyle's law approximately, the saturated vapour pressure is independent of the volume occupied and depends only on the liquid temperature.

*S.V.P. Variation with Temperature.* (i) For temperatures up to about 50°C, two barometer tubes can be used. With a little of the liquid at the top of one tube, compare the mercury level here with that in the barometer tube beside it, which has a vacuum. The S.V.P. = the difference in levels at the temperature concerned. Other temperatures are produced by using a heating coil inside a liquid surrounding the top of the tubes. (ii) For higher temperatures, a boiling method can be used. Here the external pressure outside the liquid is varied by a pump and the liquid boiling-point is measured. The S.V.P. at the boiling-point = the external pressure, read on a mercury manometer connected to the apparatus. Other S.V.P. values are obtained by adjusting the speed of the pump, which alters the external pressure.

*Dew-point.* The 'dew-point' is the temperature when moisture first condenses from the air as the air-temperature is lowered.

Measurement: Use test-tubes A and B with highly-polished silvered ends (Fig. 71). Place a little ether in A, and with the aid of a filter-pump, bubble air through R into the ether. The ether evaporates more rapidly, latent heat is taken from itself and the container, and so the silvered end becomes cooled. At one temperature, the dew-point, read on thermometer T, moisture is seen forming on C whereas D appears unchanged.

*Relative Humidity.* Definition: Relative humidity, R.H. = $m/M$ × 100%, where $m$ is the mass of water-vapour per litre of the air and $M$ is the mass of water-vapour per litre required to just saturate the air. Low relative humidity of air means that evaporation takes place readily from water. Perspiration then evaporates freely. High relative humidity means the opposite.

The mass of water-vapour per litre is proportional to the pressure of the water-vapour. Hence

$$R.H. = \frac{S.V.P. \text{ at dew-point}}{S.V.P. \text{ at air temperature}} \times 100\% \qquad \ldots(1)$$

To find relative humidity, the dew-point temperature can be measured, and then, using tables of saturation vapour pressure, the relation (1) can be applied.

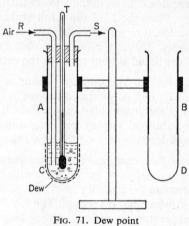

FIG. 71. Dew point

# TRANSFER OF HEAT

## Conduction

This is the transfer of heat from one point to another by the medium between them, the average positions of the layers of the medium remaining unaltered while the transfer occurs. On the molecular kinetic theory, the amplitude of the vibrating molecules of a metal, for example, increase at one end when this part of it is heated. These 'jostle' neighbouring molecules and increase their amplitude of vibration. This transfer of energy occurs all along the metal. The centre of oscillation of a molecule, or its 'mean position,' remains unaltered.

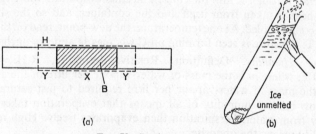

(a)                                                                    (b)

FIG. 72. Conduction of heat

*Good and Bad Conductors.* 1. *Metals have different conductivities.* To demonstrate, use long rods of the same diameter and length but different materials. Seal one end of each rod into a small metal tank, coat the rods with wax, and attach small ball-bearings as markers at equal distances along the rod. Pour boiling water into the tank: In the steady state, more balls fall from a copper rod than an iron rod, for example, showing that copper is a better conductor.

2. *Metal is a good, and water a poor, conductor.* Cover the middle part of a wooden rod with metal foil B (Fig. 72 (*a*)). Place heat-sensitive paper H firmly over the foil and part of the wood so that good contact is made. Move a burner flame to-and-fro over the paper. At X, it is practically unaffected; the heat has been conducted away quickly by the metal so that the paper temperature remains low. At Y, the paper is discoloured; the heat has not been conducted away quickly by the wood so the paper temperature rose.

3. *Water is a poor conductor.* By using metal gauze round it to make it sink, place a piece of ice at the bottom of water in a text-tube (Fig. 72 (*b*)). Heat the top of the water until it can be seen boiling. The ice remains unmelted. Heat is therefore not conducted along the water to the ice.

4. *Gas ignition temperature.* Hold a metal gauze a small distance above a bunsen burner. (i) Light the gas *above* the gauze—no flame appears between the gauze and burner. The metal conducts the heat away and the gas temperature below the gauze hence remains below the ignition temperature. (ii) Light the gas *below* the gauze—no flame appears above the gauze for a similar reason.

The miner's lamp had a burning wick surrounded by a metal gauze. This kept any inflammable gas outside the lamp below its ignition point.

Generally, liquids (except for molten metals and mercury, a moderate conductor) are poor conductors. Gases are poor conductors. Metals are good conductors. Thus iron rails feel cold on a cold day because they conduct heat quickly away from the hand; a neighbouring wooden fence does not feel so cold as heat is conducted away slowly by wood. Woollen blankets are warm as a result of pockets of *air* inside them, which acts as an insulator to the cold outside. Double glazing of windows traps air, acting as an insulator.

## Convection

This is the transfer of heat from one point of a medium to another *by movement of the medium itself* between the two points.

1. *Boiling a kettle of water.* Heat from the flame passes through the metal base of the kettle by conduction. When the bottom of the water is heated it expands and therefore becomes *less dense* (density is mass per unit volume). The water therefore rises. Its place is taken by colder

water because this is more dense. Heat is therefore carried to all parts of the water by movement or 'circulation' of water.

2. *Room radiator*. This warms a room mainly by convection—only a small amount of heat is radiated. Warm air above the hot metal radiator rises because it expands and becomes less dense. Colder air now takes its place and this also rises after warming. Heat is thus carried to different parts of the room by circulating air currents.

3. *Sea and land breezes*. The land has a smaller specific heat than that of water. On a summer day, therefore, the land reaches a higher temperature than the sea. The air above the land hence rises, cooler air from the sea moves in, and the circulation is completed in the atmosphere. This is a *sea-breeze*. At night the land cools faster than the sea. The air above the sea then rises and cooler air moves in from the land. This is a *land-breeze*.

4. *Hot-water convection system* (Fig. 73). Heat passes through the metal casing at the bottom by conduction. The hot water rises to

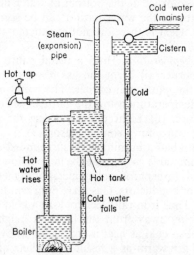

FIG. 73. Domestic convection system

the *top* of the hot tank and the cold water at the *bottom* returns to the boiler for heating. This is the 'circulating' water system. The mains supplies further cold water after hot water is drawn off. Convection takes place in gases or liquids as the movement of molecules occurs freely in fluids. It can not take place in solids.

### Radiation

This is the transfer of heat from one point to another, *without the aid of the medium between them*. In conduction and convection the medium plays an active part.

Dull-black surfaces are the best radiators. Highly-polished silvered surfaces are the worst radiators. *Experiment:* Use a metal (Leslie) cube with blackened and silvered surfaces, pour hot water into the cube, and use a thermopile and attached cone *close* to the cube to measure the radiation by a galvanometer.

Dull-black surfaces are the best absorbers and highly-polished silvered surfaces are the worst absorbers. *Experiment:* Place equal blackened and silvered plates equidistant from a hot flame between them. A small light sphere, attached behind each plate by wax, falls from the black plate and remains attached to the other. More heat per second is hence absorbed by the blackened surface.

*Properties and Nature of Radiation.* The radiation from hot objects consists of electromagnetic waves like light but of longer (invisible) wavelengths. See p. 92. Thus the radiation obeys the same properties as light rays. To show reflection, place a *hot metal ball* at the focus of a large parabolic mirror, and a *thermopile* at the focus of another parabolic mirror which receives the radiation some distance away. The deflection in the galvanometer shows that the heat rays are reflected from the mirrors in the same way as light rays.

*Vacuum or Thermos Flask.* The double-walled glass jacket contains (i) a vacuum, (ii) silvering on the inner sides (Fig. 74). The vacuum prevents heat lost by conduction and convection since no material is

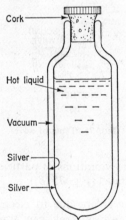

FIG. 74. Vacuum (Thermos) flask

present to transfer the heat. The silvering reduces heat losses by radiation and reflects back any which may pass through the vacuum. Insulating supports between the glass jacket and outer wall of the flask (not shown) reduces further any heat lost by conduction and absorbs shocks.

# 4 Waves

## Waves

Waves are due to *vibrations*; the direction of the wave, or ray path, is the direction of travel of the *energy* of the wave.

Types: *Water waves* are due to vibrations of particles of water—their origin is due to a disturbance such as a stone dropped into the water (Fig. 75 (*a*)).

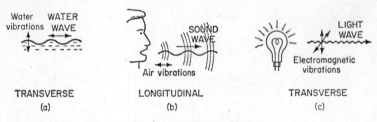

FIG. 75. Types of waves

*Sound waves* are due to vibrations of particles of air or of any other medium in which they travel (Fig. 75 (*b*)).

*Light waves* or *radio waves* are due to electromagnetic vibrations—unlike sound or water waves, they can travel through a vacuum (Fig. 75 (*c*)).

*Transverse Waves.* These are waves in which the direction of the wave is *perpendicular* to the direction of the vibrations.

*Examples.* 1. A water wave due to a stone dropped in spreads horizontally; the water particles vibrate vertically (Fig. 75 (*a*)).

2. A plucked loose horizontal coil, or a plucked violin string, vibrates perpendicularly to the wave, which travels horizontally (Fig. 76).

3. Light waves or radio waves are due to electromagnetic vibrations perpendicular to their direction of travel (Fig. 75 (*c*)).

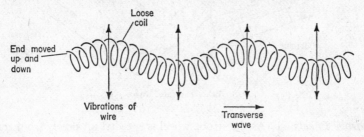

FIG. 76. Transverse wave

*Longitudinal Waves*. These are waves in which the direction of the wave is in the *same* direction as the vibrations.

*Examples.*    1. If a loose horizontal coil is set into vibration horizontally, the wave travels horizontally (Fig. 77).

2. Sound waves in air travel in the same direction as the vibrations —see Fig. 75 (*b*).

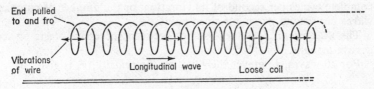

FIG. 77. Longitudinal wave

*Wave Velocity.*    This is the *distance travelled per second* by the wave.

Sound waves in air travel with a velocity of about 340 metre (1100 ft) per sec. All electromagnetic waves, such as light or radio waves, travel with a velocity of about 300 million ($3 \times 10^8$) metres per sec (186,000 miles per sec) through empty space.

*Measurement of velocity of water waves.*    Use a hand strobe S with say 12 slits to observe the water waves (Fig. 78). Increase the strobe speed from zero until the waves first appear stationary. Measure the length occupied by several waves with a ruler R and hence the wavelength $\lambda$. Measure the number of revolutions of the strobe in a given time, and hence determine the frequency of the wave. Calculate the velocity from $V = f\lambda$ (p. 90).

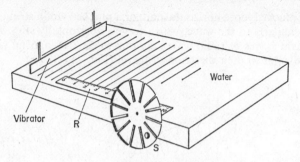

FIG. 78. Water waves

*Strobe Effects* 1. As the strobe wheel is speeded up slowly from zero, the waves are at first seen advancing and at one stage become stationary. The wave now travels a whole number of wavelengths in the time between successive glimpses.

2. As the speed of the strobe is increased further, the waves are seen at shorter time-intervals. They appear stationary again as the speed is increased twice as fast as in 1. When the waves appear stationary at the fastest speed, the wave travels one wavelength between successive glimpses. Thus $\lambda$ can be measured by the ruler R in Fig. 78.

*Frequency, Wavelength.* The *frequency*, $f$, of a wave is the number of complete cycles per second of its vibration, or the number of complete waves per second passing a given point.

The *wavelength*, $\lambda$, is the distance between successive crests or successive troughs.

For all waves, whatever their nature, the *velocity*, $V$, is given by

$$V = f\lambda$$

Proof: In one second, $f$ waves travel out since $f$ is the frequency of vibration. Each wave occupies a distance $\lambda$. Hence the total distance travelled per second $= V = f\lambda$.

*Long and Short Wavelengths. Sound waves.* In air, the velocity is about 340 metre per sec. Frequencies of sound waves may range from about 20 to 16,000 Hz (1 Hz = 1 cycle per sec or c/s). From $V = f\lambda$, the wavelength $\lambda$ for a whistle of 1000 Hz is given by

$$\lambda = \frac{V}{f} = \frac{340}{1000} \text{ metre} = 0.34 \text{ m} = 34 \text{ cm}$$

Note the order of the wavelength of sound, which is relatively long.

*Light Waves.* Wavelengths range from about $4 \times 10^{-5}$ cm (violet) to $7 \times 10^{-5}$ cm (red). Note the order of the wavelength, which is relatively short or about 500,000 times shorter than sound waves in air. From $V = f\lambda$, since $V = 3 \times 10^{10}$ cm per sec for light waves, the frequency for yellow light of wavelength $6 \times 10^{-5}$ cm is given by

$$f = \frac{V}{\lambda} = \frac{3 \times 10^{10}}{6 \times 10^{-5}} = 5 \times 10^{14} \text{ Hz}$$

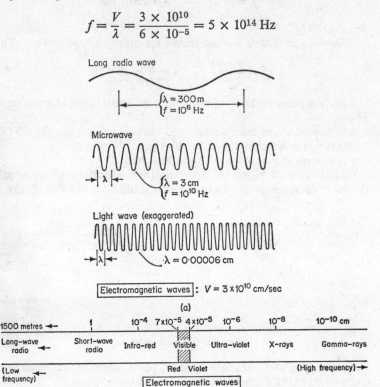

FIG. 79. Types of electromagnetic waves

*Electromagnetic Waves. Radio waves.* Since $V = 3 \times 10^8$ metre/sec, a long wavelength such as 1500 metres has a frequency given by

$$f = \frac{V}{\lambda} = \frac{3 \times 10^8}{1500} = 200,000 \text{ Hz}$$

A medium wavelength such as 300 metres has a higher frequency given by

$$f = \frac{V}{\lambda} = \frac{3 \times 10^8}{300} = 1,000,000 \ (10^6) \text{ Hz} \quad \text{or} \quad 1 \text{ MHz (megahertz)}$$

*Microwaves.* Radio waves of 3 cm wavelength have frequencies given by

$$f = \frac{V}{\lambda} = \frac{3 \times 10^8}{0 \cdot 03} = 10^{10} \text{ Hz}$$

See Fig. 79 (*a*).

*Infra-red* waves have wavelengths of the order $10^{-4}$ cm and less. Thus

$$f = \frac{V}{\lambda} = \frac{3 \times 10^8}{10^{-6}} = 3 \times 10^{14} \text{ Hz}$$

*Light waves,* or *visible spectrum.* Note the small range of wavelengths above.

*Ultra-violet waves* have wavelengths about $10^{-6}$ cm. See Fig. 79 (*a*).

*X-rays* have wavelengths about $10^{-8}$ cm.

$\gamma$ (*gamma*)-*rays* have wavelengths less than $10^{-8}$ cm.

Observe that the higher the frequency (or the shorter the wavelength), the more energetic is the electromagnetic radiation. See Fig. 79 (*b*).

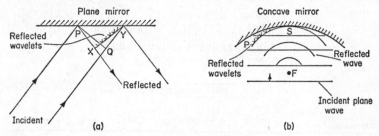

FIG. 80. Reflection of waves

*Reflection of Waves.* At *plane surfaces*, plane waves are reflected at an angle equal to the angle of incidence (Fig. 80 (*a*)).

Reason: When the wavefront reaches the position PQ, the point P on it becomes a 'centre of disturbance' which emits wavelets. This reaches X in the time Q takes to reach Y, so that PX = QY. The reflected wavelets lie on XY, and XY and PQ make equal angles with the reflecting surface.

At curved concave spherical surfaces, incident plane waves converge to a point F, the principal focus (p. 111). Fig. 80 (*b*). Note that P reflects wavelets while the plane wave continues to travel to S.

*Refraction of Waves.*   *Water waves.* Place a glass plate just below the surface and observe the reduction in speed (refraction) in the shallow water.

*Microwaves.* Use liquid paraffin in a 60° hollow prism, or a paraffin-wax 60° prism to refract the waves. With a 90°, 45°, 45° paraffin-wax prism, total internal reflection is obtained.

Light waves are refracted by water or glass; sound waves are refracted by a balloon filled with carbon dioxide, which acts as a 'lens'.

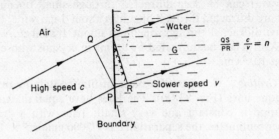

FIG. 81. Refraction of waves

Refraction, the change in direction of waves passing from one medium to another, is due to a *change in velocity*. Explanation: when a plane wavefront PQ reaches the plane boundary with a different medium G, for example, from air to water, P emits wavelets which may travel with a smaller velocity in G (Fig. 81). Thus when the wave from Q reaches the boundary at S, the wavelet from P reaches R. Hence the wavefront SR in G changes in direction. Note that:

$$QS/PR = \text{speed in air } c/\text{speed in water } v = n,$$

where $n$ is the refractive index of water (p. 116).

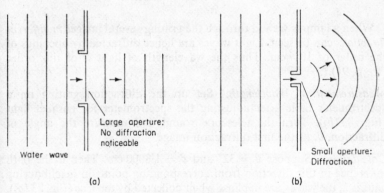

FIG. 82. Diffraction of waves

*Diffraction.* When the width of an opening is large compared to the wavelength, $\lambda$, there is negligible diffraction—the wave travels straight through in the same direction (rectilinear propagation) (Fig. 82 (a)). When the width of an opening is comparable to $\lambda$, the wave spreads round the opening on passing through—diffraction is considerable

(Fig. 82 (*b*)). Thus (i) sound waves can be heard round corners through open doors—their long wavelengths are comparable to the door width, (ii) water waves can be seen diffracted through small openings, (iii) microwaves are diffracted through openings about 1 cm wide, (iv) light waves can be diffracted through openings about 1/2000 cm wide (see below), (v) X-rays can be diffracted by atoms in crystals whose separation is about $10^{-8}$ cm.

*Diffraction Grating.* Consists of a piece of film containing many fine parallel opaque lines (Fig. 83 (*a*)). The lines have equal thickness and their separation is constant and very small. Thus with a grating of 2000 lines per centimetre, the separation *d* is 1/2000 cm or $5 \times 10^{-4}$ cm.

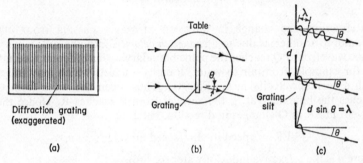

(a)    (b)    (c)

FIG. 83. Diffraction of light waves

When a lamp is viewed through the grating several images *in different directions* can be seen. Light waves are hence diffracted by openings of the order of $10^{-4}$ cm. Thus the wavelength of light is of this order (see p. 91).

*Measurement of Wavelength.* Set up the diffraction grating on a spectrometer table after adjusting the spectrometer for parallel light (Fig. 83 (*b*)). Turn the telescope round and measure the angle of diffraction, $\theta$, of the first diffraction image.

*Calculation.* Suppose $\theta = 32°$ and $d = 1/8000$ cm. Then if the path difference in this direction from corresponding points in neighbouring gaps is $\lambda$, the waves are in phase when collected by the lens (Fig. 83 (*c*)). This also applies to all other pairs of corresponding points in the two gaps. The path difference is $d \sin \theta$. Thus $\lambda = d \sin \theta = (1/8000) \times \sin 32° = 6 \times 10^{-5}$ cm.

If two corresponding parallel rays in neighbouring clear spaces have a path difference of $2\lambda$ in a different direction, then these waves also arrive in phase at the focus of a lens turned to collect them. Waves from all other corresponding points arrive in phase too, since they too have a path difference of $2\lambda$. Hence a bright diffraction image is seen in another direction $\theta_1$, where $d \sin \theta_1 = 2\lambda$, assuming $d$ is greater than $2\lambda$ so that $\sin \theta_1$ is less than 1. Similarly, another bright diffraction image may be obtained in a direction $\theta_2$, where $d \sin \theta_2 = 3\lambda$.

*Interference.* Two waves interfere with each other where their paths cross. With *constructive* interference, the resultant wave has an amplitude equal to the sum of those of the two waves. With *destructive* interference, the two waves are opposite in phase; and if the amplitudes of the waves are equal, the resultant is then zero.

*Sound waves.* Two nearly-equal tuning forces, sounding together, produce a rise and fall in intensity called 'beats'. Interference takes place periodically.

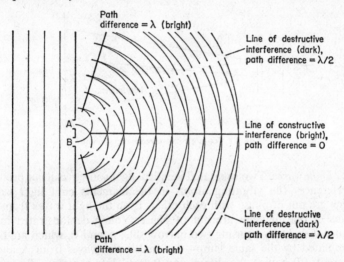

FIG. 84. Interference of waves

*Water waves.* Two close small vibrators dipping into water, or two close slits with plane waves incident on them, produce an interference pattern. Note that:

(1) Permanent destructive and constructive interference occurs along lines where the path difference is $\lambda/2$ and $\lambda$ respectively (Fig. 84). At other lines, destructive interference occurs when the path difference is an odd number of half-wavelengths and constructive interference when the path difference is a whole number of wavelengths.

(2) When the two sources A, B are moved *closer together*, the lines of destructive and constructive interference move further apart and are more easily recognisable. When A and B are moved *farther apart*, the lines become closer and more difficult to recognise.

*Coherent Sources.    Young's experiment.* Two sources of vibration can produce a permanent interference effect only if they are *coherent* sources, that is, they have the same frequency and are *always in phase (or have a constant phase difference).* One method of producing two coherent sources with short radio waves or with light waves is to place a source behind, and equidistant from, two parallel openings or slits.

1. *Microwaves.* Place a 3-cm microwave generator behind two parallel openings A, B a few centimetres apart. A, B act as two coherent sources and interference is detected by a microammeter in the receiver circuit. The wavelength $\lambda$ can be measured from the first position, P say, of constructive interference, since $PA - PB = \lambda$, where A, B are the two slits.

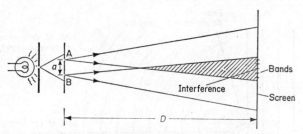

Fig. 85. Young's interference experiment

2. *Light waves.* Two separated identical light sources can *not* produce interference—the vibrating atoms in the filaments emit light waves which are out of phase with each other. Even the light waves from the atoms of one filament are out of phase. Young demonstrated interference of light by (i) using two narrow slits, A and B, which are both illuminated by the same lamp—this makes the waves from A and B coherent, (ii) having the slits A and B very close together—the wavelength of light is extremely small (p. 91) and the bright and dark bands would overlap if the slits are wide apart so that only a uniform brightness would be seen (Fig. 85).

In the laboratory, use a bright line source of light such as a motor headlamp with a slit in front, two parallel slits close together (e.g. 0·5 mm) and a white screen.

*Calculation.* If $a$ is the slit separation, $y$ is the separation between consecutive bands, and $D$ is the screen distance from the slits, then

$\lambda/a$ = angle from normal at which the first bright band is formed
    $= y/D$

Hence $\lambda = ay/D$. If $a = 0\cdot4$ mm $= 0\cdot04$ cm, $D = 100$ cm, $y = 1\cdot5$ mm $= 0\cdot15$ cm, then $\lambda = 0\cdot04 \times 0\cdot15/100 = 6/10^5 = 6 \times 10^{-5}$ cm.

Red light (using red filter) produces bands more widely spaced than blue light (using blue filter). Thus, since $\lambda \propto y$ (separation), the wavelength of red light is longer than that of blue light.

*Stationary Waves.* Produced by interference between two waves travelling in opposite directions which have the same frequency and amplitude.

*Examples.* Transverse stationary wave along plucked string or vibrating thread (Fig. 86 (*a*)). Transverse and longitudinal stationary waves along a vibrating loose coil ('slinky') held at one end (Fig. 86 (*b*)).

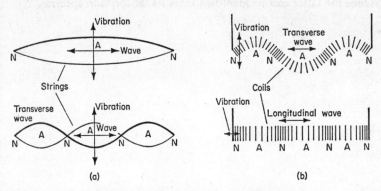

FIG. 86. Longitudinal and transverse waves

*Definition.* A stationary wave is one in which some points called *nodes*, N, are permanently at rest, points half-way between are vibrating with maximum amplitude A, and others between the nodes are vibrating in phase but with smaller amplitude.

Distance AA = $\lambda/2$, NN = $\lambda/2$, NA = $\lambda/4$.

*Resonance.* A vibrating system can be set into vibration by an *external* periodic force.

Experiment: Suspend five pendula from a horizontal string, each of a different length. Suspend another pendulum A from the same string carrying a heavy weight and equal in length to one pendulum B. Start A vibrating; observe that only B vibrates through a large amplitude.

Conclusion: A vibrating system with a natural frequency $f_0$ has the largest amplitude of vibration when it is subjected to a periodic force of exactly the same frequency. The system is then said to be 'in resonance'.

*Applications of Resonance. Mechanical.* Spring boards or trampolines provide added 'lift' when set into resonance by repeated impulses of the same frequency as their natural frequency.

*Electrical.* Radio receivers are 'tuned' and then set into resonance by waves from distant radio transmitters. 'Tuning' changes the frequency of the receiver circuit to that of the distant transmitter.

*Optical.* Fine dark lines are observed across parts of the sun's visible spectrum. They are called *absorption lines.* Explanation: The cooler parts of the sun's atmosphere contain atoms which are set into resonance by light from the hot part of the sun. The vibrating atoms re-emit light, but this is spread out in all directions so that the intensity of the light sent in a particular direction to an observer on the earth is reduced.

Note that the wavelength corresponding to the absorption line is exactly the same as that which would be emitted by the absorbing atom. Hence the latter can be identified from its 'absorption spectra'.

# 5 Sound

## Sound and Medium

Sound waves always require a medium or matter in which they travel. Demonstrated by sealing an electric bell into a bell-jar, starting the bell ringing, and then pumping out the air. The sound gradually dies down but the clapper can still be seen striking the gong. Allow the air to return; the sound is heard again.

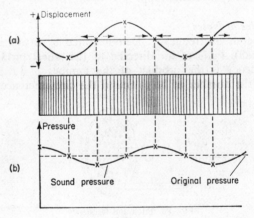

FIG. 87. Sound wave in air

## Wave-motion

The energetic though small vibrations of a sounding tuning-fork can be detected by bringing near one prong a suspended pith or cork ball. On contact with the prong the ball flies off violently.

When a wave travels in air from a tuning-fork to the ear, each layer or particle vibrates to-and-fro at the same frequency (Fig. 87). The displacement (distance from mean position) at a particular layer follows

99

a simple harmonic change. Since sound takes time to travel from place to place, layers near each other are vibrating out of phase. Layers spaced one wavelength, $\lambda$, apart are in phase.

'Freeze' the wave at any instant—the displacements at different points in the medium vary in a simple harmonic manner (Fig. 87 (*a*)). 'Unfreeze' the wave—the pattern changes, although still simple harmonic in profile, and the wave or energy travels forward.

Waves can be discussed by reference *either* to 'displacement' changes *or* to 'pressure' changes (Fig. 87 (*b*)). The carbon microphone is sensitive to pressure changes.

### Velocity

As on p. 90, velocity of sound, $V = f\lambda$, where $f$ is the frequency (number of vibrations per second) and $\lambda$ is the wavelength (distance between successive crests). In gases such as air, the velocity is *independent* of the pressure but it increases as the temperature rises. Velocity in air at normal temperature is about 340 metres per second. It can be measured *either* by a resonance tube experiment (p. 103) *or* by a microphone and cathode-ray oscillograph experiment.

The velocity of sound, $V$, is greater in liquids than in air; in water, $V$ is 1500 metres per second (approx.).

### Characteristics of Notes

1. *Pitch* depends on frequency. Demonstrated by a rotating Seebeck wheel (Fig. 88). Puffs of air directed at the wheel produce a note whose frequency is the product of the number of revolutions per second and the number of holes round the circumference. The pitch

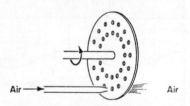

FIG. 88. Pitch and frequency

rises as either the speed of the rotation or number of holes is increased. When the number of holes is doubled, a note one octave higher is heard.

2. *Loudness* of a note depends on the *square of its amplitude* because the energy depends on this factor. A soft sound has a small amplitude; a loud sound has a large amplitude. The larger the mass of air set into vibration, the louder is the sound. A sounding tuning-fork in air produces a soft sound; but if it is placed with the shank (handle) on

the table a much louder sound is heard, as the large mass of air in contact with the table is set into vibration.

3. *Quality* or *timbre* of a note depends on the *overtones* accompanying the main or fundamental note. 'Overtones' are notes of higher frequency than the fundamental but with smaller amplitude. They provide a background which the ear detects.

If the waveform of a note is a sine wave, as in the case of the tuning-fork, only one (pure) note is heard. The waveform of the same note played on the piano or violin has a relatively irregular waveform—other notes are present besides the main or fundamental note.

### Reflection, Refraction

1. *Echoes* are due to reflection of sound waves. Reflection may be shown in the laboratory using a source of sound, a straight tube to define the direction of sound waves, a smooth board or metal reflector, and a straight tube with microphone connected to a cathode-ray oscillograph as a detector.

2. On very hot days, sounds are not heard over as long a distance as on cooler days. Waves at ground level travel faster than those higher up since the temperature here is higher, and so refraction of sound occurs away from the ground. In the laboratory, refraction may be demonstrated with the aid of a source of sound, a large balloon filled with carbon dioxide which acts as a 'convex lens', and a microphone with cathode-ray oscillograph as a detector.

## VIBRATIONS IN PIPES

Pipe or string instruments (p. 104) produce *stationary waves* when played. A stationary wave is one in which some points, nodes N, are permanently at rest; points half-way between are vibrating with maximum amplitude, antinodes A; and the other points between A and N are vibrating with smaller amplitude (Fig. 89 (i)). See p. 97. Observe and memorize that, if $\lambda$ is the wavelength,

*distance between consecutive antinodes, AA, or nodes, NN,* $= \lambda/2$

and

*distance between neighbouring nodes and antinodes, NA,* $= \lambda/4$

### Closed Pipe

When sounded, a stationary wave is set up by reflection at either end of the pipe. Remember that a node N is always formed at the closed end because the air here cannot move; and that an antinode A is always formed at the open end because the air here is most free to move.

Possible stationary waves in the air are shown in Fig. 89. The lowest note or *fundamental*, frequency $f_0$, is produced by blowing gently (Fig.

89 (*b*)). The antinode A is actually a small distance above the end of the pipe but we ignore this for the present. Then, if $l$ = length of pipe,

$$l = NA = \lambda/4 \quad \text{or} \quad \lambda = 4l$$

$$\therefore f_0 = \frac{V}{\lambda} = \frac{V}{4l} \qquad \ldots\text{(i)}$$

where $V$ is the velocity of sound in the air.

In Fig. 89 (*b*), the wavelength is three times as *small* as in Fig. 89 (*a*); thus the frequency here, $f_1 = 3f_0$. In Fig. 89 (*d*), the frequency is $5f_0$.

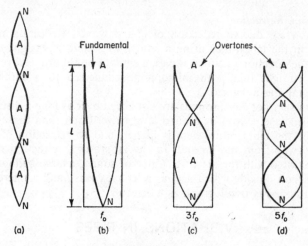

FIG. 89. Stationary waves in pipes

Thus the possible overtones in the closed pipe are $3f_0, 5f_0, 7f_0, \ldots$, or the *odd harmonics*. (A 'harmonic' is a note which is a simple multiple of the fundamental note $f_0$; for example, $f_0$ is the first harmonic, $2f_0$ is the second harmonic, and so on.)

*End-correction.* The actual distance outside the end of the pipe is called the 'end-correction', $c$. Note that it is a 'correction' or *addition* to the measured length $l$, so that

$$l + c = NA = \lambda/4$$

Thus, more correctly,

$$f_0 = \frac{V}{\lambda} = \frac{V}{4(l + c)} \qquad \ldots\text{(ii)}$$

It should be noted from (i) or (ii) that the pitch or fundamental frequency $f_0$ rises when the air temperature rises since $V$ then increases.

Further, $f_0 \propto 1/l$ approximately, so that a pipe of length 80 cm produces a note about *half* the frequency of one from a pipe 40 cm long.

*Velocity Measurement.    Resonance tube.* Experiment: Using a water reservoir X, slowly lower the level of water from the top of a tube Y (Fig. 90). At the same time, place a sounding tuning-fork F of frequency

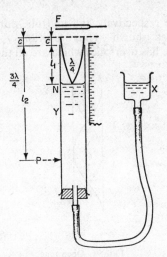

FIG. 90. Resonance tube experiment

512 Hz over Y so that sound waves travel down Y. At one level, N, the loudest sound is heard—the air is set into resonance by the fork (p. 97). Measure the length $l_1$ from N to the top of the tube. Move X lower until a second resonance position P is obtained. Measure the distance $l_2$ from P to the top of the tube.

*Calculation.*   $l_1 + c = \lambda/4$, $l_2 + c = 3\lambda/4$,

$$\therefore l_2 - l_1 = \frac{3\lambda}{4} - \frac{\lambda}{4} = \frac{\lambda}{2}$$

$$\therefore \lambda = 2(l_2 - l_1)$$

$$\therefore V = f\lambda = 2f(l_2 - l_1)$$

Thus the velocity of sound in the air in the tube can be calculated, knowing $f$, $l_1$ and $l_2$.

### Open Pipes

These are pipes open at both ends. When sounded, antinodes A are always set up at both ends. Possible stationary waves are shown in Fig. 91.

For the lowest or fundamental frequency, $f_0$, neglecting end-corrections,

$$\text{length of pipe, } l_1 = AA = \lambda/2 \quad \text{or} \quad \lambda = 2l$$

$$\therefore f_0 = \frac{V}{\lambda} = \frac{V}{2l}$$

The overtones have respectively half and one-third the wavelength of the fundamental, as shown. Thus $f_1 = 2f_0$, $f_2 = 3f_0$, and so on. Hence the open pipe has overtones which are all the possible harmonics of $f_0$ (p. 102).

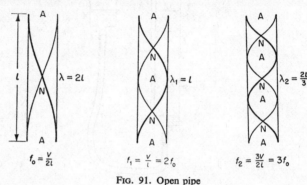

FIG. 91. Open pipe

*Example.* A pipe closed at one end is blown gently. What note is produced if its length is 34 cm? If the end-correction is taken into account and is 1 cm, what note would then be obtained? (Velocity of sound in air = 340 m per sec.)

The wavelength, $\lambda = 4 \times 34 = 136$ cm, since length of pipe = $\lambda/4$ (p. 102),

$$\therefore \text{frequency, } f = \frac{V}{\lambda} = \frac{340 \times 100}{136} = 250 \text{ Hz} \qquad \ldots(1)$$

With the end-correction, $\lambda/4 = 34 + 1 = 35$ cm,

$$\therefore \lambda = 4 \times 35 = 140 \text{ cm}$$

$$\therefore \text{new frequency, } f = \frac{V}{\lambda} = \frac{340 \times 100}{140}$$

$$= 243 \text{ Hz (approx.)} \qquad \ldots(2)$$

## VIBRATIONS IN STRINGS

Plucked or bowed strings, as in the violin, produce *transverse* waves along the string (Fig. 92). (Compare the sounding *pipe*, p. 102, which produces *longitudinal* waves.) Stationary transverse waves are set up by reflection at either fixed end. Note carefully that both ends are always *nodes*, N, because they cannot move.

*Frequencies.* Possible stationary waves, produced by plucking in the middle of a string, are shown in Fig. 92. The lowest or *fundamental frequency*, $f_0$ (Fig. 92 (a)), corresponds to a wavelength $\lambda$ given by

$$\text{length of string, } l = NN = \lambda/2 \quad \text{or} \quad \lambda = 2l$$

$$\therefore f_0 = \frac{V}{2l} \qquad \qquad \ldots \text{(i)}$$

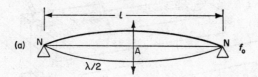

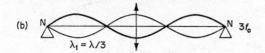

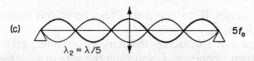

FIG. 92. Stationary waves in string

where $V$ is the velocity of the *transverse wave along the string*. Observe that the wave is due to vibrating particles of string dancing up and down, whereas the wave in a sounding pipe is due to vibrating particles of air (p. 101). Further, unlike the wave in a pipe, there is no 'end-correction' at the string.

From Fig. 92 (b), the first overtone has a wavelength one-third that of the fundamental; thus $f_1 = 3f_0$. From Fig. 92 (c), the second overtone has a frequency $f_2 = 5f_0$. The overtones are thus the odd harmonics of $f_0$ when the string is plucked in the middle.

*Velocity of Wave.* The velocity $V$ depends on (i) the *tension*, $T$, in the string, (ii) its *mass per unit length*, $m$. Generally,

$$V = \sqrt{T/m}$$

$$\therefore f = \text{fundamental frequency } f_0 = V/\lambda$$

$$= \frac{1}{2l} \sqrt{\frac{T}{m}} \qquad \qquad \ldots \text{(ii)}$$

Thus $f$ is (i) inversely-proportional to the length (halving the length doubles the frequency), (ii) proportional to the square root of the tension (increasing the tension four times doubles the frequency), (iii) inversely-proportional to the square root of the mass per unit length (increasing the wire density four times will halve the frequency).

*Sonometer Experiment.* The *sonometer* S is a hollow box with a long wire PQ and moveable bridges B, C (Fig. 93). The distance apart of the bridges can be read on a horizontal millimetre scale M below. By

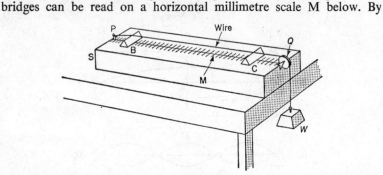

FIG. 93. Sonometer

attaching a weight $W$ to one end, a tension of this magnitude can be applied to the wire.

1. *To show $f \propto 1/l$.* Keep the tension constant, take five tuning-forks of known frequency, $f$, and tune the wire to each fork in turn by moving a bridge. Measure the five lengths $l$.

Plot a graph of $1/l$ v. $f$. It is found to be a straight line *passing through the origin.* Hence, for a given tension and wire, $f \propto 1/l$.

2. *Tension.* Keeping the length constant, add weights at stages to increase the tension and pluck the wire—the frequency increases. When the tension is increased four times, a note one octave higher is heard.

3. *Mass per unit length.* Change the wire to a thinner wire, keeping the tension and length constant. A note of higher frequency is hence obtained when the mass per unit length decreases.

*Frequency Measurement.* The unknown frequency, $f$, of a tuning-fork can be found by first tuning the sonometer wire to it. Suppose the length is 46·2 cm. Then tune the wire to a fork of known frequency, say 480 Hz. Suppose the length is now 50·4 cm. Then, since $f \propto 1/l$ for a given tension and wire,

$$\frac{f}{480} = \frac{1/46 \cdot 2}{1/50 \cdot 4} = \frac{50 \cdot 4}{46 \cdot 2}$$

$$\therefore f = \frac{50 \cdot 4}{46 \cdot 2} \times 480 = 524 \text{ Hz}$$

Note that, unlike the case of the resonance tube experiment, there is no 'end-connection' to apply. The sonometer thus provides a more accurate measurement of an unknown frequency.

*Examples.* 1. A note of frequency 512 Hz is obtained from a plucked wire of length 40 cm. What length of the same wire produces a frequency of 320 Hz?

Since $f \propto 1/l$, a longer wire produces a *smaller* frequency. In this case,

$$\frac{512}{320} = \frac{1/40}{1/l} = \frac{l}{40}$$

$$\therefore l = 40 \times \frac{512}{320} = 64 \text{ cm}$$

2. A note is obtained from a plucked wire when the tension is 4 N. What additional weight is needed to produce a note one octave higher from the same length of wire?

Suppose $T$ is the required new tension. The new frequency is twice the original frequency. Since $f \propto \sqrt{T}$,

$$\therefore \frac{2}{1} = \frac{\sqrt{T}}{\sqrt{4}}$$

$$\therefore \sqrt{T} = 4 \quad \text{or} \quad T = 16 \text{ N}$$

$$\therefore \text{additional weight} = 16 - 4 = 12 \text{ N}$$

3. The temperature rises in the neighbourhood of (1) a pipe, (ii) a sonometer. What is the effect on the frequency obtained in each case?

(i) The frequency, $f = V/\lambda$, where $\lambda$ is related to the length of the pipe. The temperature rise increases the velocity $V$ of sound in air relatively much more than the increase in the length of pipe. Thus the frequency rises.

(ii) The frequency, $f = \frac{1}{2l}\sqrt{\frac{T}{m}}$. The temperature rise makes the wire sag, thus decreasing the tension $T$. Hence the frequency is lowered.

# 6 Optics

## RECTILINEAR PROPAGATION

### Rectilinear Propagation

If an opening is large compared with the wavelength of light (p. 93), the light passes through in a straight line (rectilinear propagation).

Demonstration: Use a candle flame or light in front of a large pin-hole O, and line up two other pin-holes, P and Q, so that the light can be seen through them. Pass a thread through O, P and Q, and draw it taut. Observe that the thread is straight.

*Shadows.* 1. An opaque object cuts off light rays so that a shadow of it is formed. A full-shadow region is called the *umbra*; a partial-shadow region is called the *penumbra*.

2. A *small* light source in front of an opaque object produces a sharp shadow of the object. A *large* light source produces both umbra and penumbra, as in the sun's eclipse (Fig. 94 (*a*)).

3. *Eclipse of sun.* This occurs when the moon passes between the sun and the earth. 'Total eclipse' is seen from the umbra U; 'partial eclipse' from the penumbra P (Fig. 94 (*a*)). An 'annular eclipse' is seen from A in Fig. 94 (*b*) when the moon and earth are in different positions from that in Fig. 94 (*a*). The rim of the sun is now seen.

### Pin-hole Camera.

This has a small pin-hole on one side of a closed box, and a light-sensitive film or screen on the other side. (i) If the hole is *small*, every point in the image corresponds to a particular point on the object and a *sharp inverted image* is obtained. (ii) If several pin-holes are made, each produces its own image; blurring occurs due to overlap. (iii) If the hole is large, an *area* on the image is illuminated by a particular point on the object, so that overlapping occurs; the image is blurred. Note that a suitable convex lens in front of several pin-holes or a large hole produces a *sharp* image (p. 121). No matter

108

where the ray from a point on the object strikes the central part of the lens, it is brought by refraction of the lens to the same point image.

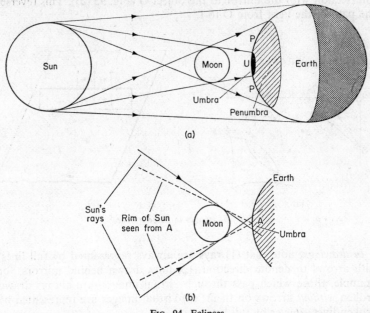

(a)

(b)

FIG. 94. Eclipses

## REFLECTION AT PLANE SURFACES

*Laws.* (1) The incident and reflected rays and the normal all lie in one plane. (2) The angle of incidence = the angle of reflection.

Note that part of the incident light is always reflected from boundaries such as air–water or air–glass.

*Images. Experiment to locate a point image I.* (1) O represents a pin (Fig. 95 (*a*)). Observe the image I, and place two other pins A, B and C, D in line with I. Remove the mirror and produce BA and DC to meet. They intersect behind the mirror at I.

(2) Place a pin L behind the mirror (Fig. 95 (*b*)). View the image of O in the mirror and the upper part of L, and move L until, on moving the head from side to side, the image and L appear to stay together as shown or have 'no parallax'. Then L is at the same place as the image.

Observe that (i) diverging rays such as OL and OM from a point object O are reflected as a *diverging beam* from the mirror, (ii) *the image I is as far behind the mirror as the object O is in front.* (Fig. 95(*a*)).

The latter result can be proved geometrically from congruency of triangles in Fig. 95 (*a*).

*Drawing Images.* *To show the beam of rays which reach the edge,* first join the boundary of the eye to the image, I, and then join the points of intersection with the mirror to the object O (Fig. 95 (*a*)). This reverses the path of the light from O to I.

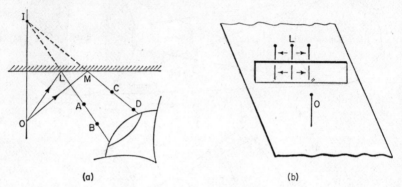

FIG. 95. Images in plane mirror

*In drawings,* note that (1) rays are always represented by full lines, with arrows to denote direction; (2) lines drawn behind mirrors, for example, those which pass through virtual images, are always drawn broken *without* arrows on them; (3) virtual images are represented by broken lines—never by full lines.

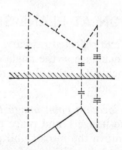

FIG. 96. Image in plane mirror

*Large Object.* A large object, represented by a letter F, has an image behind a plane mirror (Fig. 96). This can be drawn by taking any point on F, marking its image at an equal perpendicular distance behind the mirror as shown, and then repeating for several other points on F.

Result: The image in the plane mirror is (i) virtual, (ii) erect, (iii) the same size as the object, (iv) laterally inverted, (v) as far behind the mirror as the object is in front.

*Lateral inversion* means that the right side of the object appears as the left side of the image. Hence (*a*) the writing on blotting paper can be read when it is held up to a plane mirror, (*b*) a right-handed person holding a tennis racket in front of a mirror appears to be left-handed.

# CURVED MIRRORS

## Spherical and Parabolic Mirrors

Curved mirrors may be spherical (driving, shaving and dentist's magnifying mirror) or parabolic in shape (searchlight, motor-headlamp).

A *wide* parallel beam of light is not brought to a point focus by a spherical mirror but by a parabolic mirror. Conversely, with a bright lamp at its principal focus a spherical mirror does not reflect all the light incident on it in a parallel beam, so that the intensity of the beam diminishes with distance. A parabolic mirror is used for a searchlight or headlamp. In spherical mirrors, which we discuss now, remember that only the central part can produce a parallel beam.

## Definitions

1. The *pole*, P, is the middle point of the spherical mirror (Fig. 97).

2. The *centre of curvature*, C, is the centre of the sphere of which the mirror was part.

3. The *principal axis* is the line joining P and C. A *secondary axis* is a line parallel to PC.

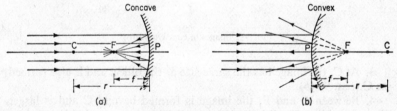

FIG. 97. Reflection of parallel rays

4. *Radius of curvature*, *r*, is the distance PC.

5. *Principal focus of* (i) *concave mirror*. This is the point F on the principal axis to which rays *parallel and close* to the principal axis converge after reflection from the mirror (Fig. 97 (*a*)); the concave mirror has a *real* focus. (ii) *Convex mirror*. This is the point F on the principal axis from which rays, parallel and close to the principal axis, appear to diverge after reflection from the mirror, the convex mirror has a virtual focus (Fig. 97 (*b*)).

6. *Focal length, f*, is the distance from P to F.

In both concave and convex mirrors, $r = 2f$ or $f = r/2$.

*Drawing Images.* For large drawings, (i) represent the curved mirror by a straight line, (ii) draw a ray from the top point of the object parallel to the principal axis—the reflected ray passes through F, (iii) draw a ray *either* through C—this is reflected straight back since it strikes the mirror normally, *or* through F—this is reflected parallel to the principal axis. The image of the top point of the object is the point of intersection of the two lines. Remember that arrows are required on all rays to show how they travel, but *not* on the dotted lines behind the mirror which pass through a virtual image.

## Images in Concave Mirror

1. An object O a long way from this mirror has a *real, inverted* and *small* image at the focus.

2. As O approaches the mirror the image grows in size. Beyond C, the image is real, inverted and small (Fig. 98 (*a*)).

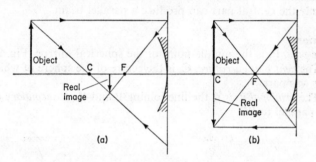

FIG. 98. Images in concave mirror

3. At C, the image has the same size as the object and is also formed at C (Fig. 98 (*b*)).

4. Between C and F, the image is formed beyond C and is larger than the object (Fig. 99 (*a*)). Observe that the image and object may be interchanged in positions.

5. *Magnified erect image.* This is obtained with the object between F and P, that is, the object is nearer to the mirror than the focal length (Fig. 99 (*b*)). Observe that the image is virtual and erect, whereas the magnified image obtained in Fig. 99 (*a*) was real and inverted. Fig. 99 (*b*) illustrates the principle of the shaving mirror and dentist's mirror.

## Images in Convex Mirror

Remember that the principal focus and centre of curvature of a convex mirror is *behind* the mirror, or virtual; and that all lines drawn behind the mirror are drawn broken and with no arrows on them.

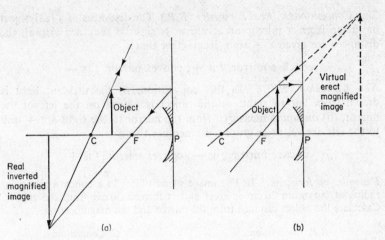

FIG. 99. Magnified images in concave mirror: (a) inverted, real (c) upright, virtual

The image is always *virtual, erect* and *diminished* (Fig. 100 (*a*)). Besides the advantage of an erect image, the convex mirror has the advantage of a wide field of view—a driver can see objects in a wide angle round the mirror (Fig. 100 (*b*)).

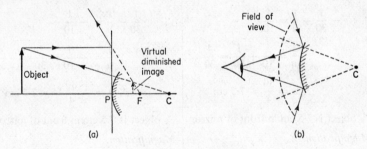

FIG. 100. Convex mirror

## Mirror Formulae

1. Relation between *r* and *f*: $r = 2f$ or $f = r/2$.

2. Object and image relation: $\dfrac{1}{v} + \dfrac{1}{u} = \dfrac{1}{f}$.

3. Linear (transverse) magnification: $m = \dfrac{u}{v}$.

*Sign Conventions.*    *Real is positive* (*R.P.*). The distances of a real object or image from a mirror are given a + sign; if they are virtual, the distances are given a − sign. Remember that:

concave mirror, $f$ is + ; convex mirror, $f$ is −

*New Cartesian* (*N.C.*).   In this convention, (i) the incident light is drawn from left to right, or the object is placed on the left of the mirror, (ii) distances measured from the mirror to the right are + and to the left are −, as in graphs. Remember that:

concave mirror, $f$ is − ; convex mirror, $f$ is +

*Examples on formulae.*   **1.** The image of an object in a concave mirror of radius of curvature 20 cm is erect and is formed 30 cm from the mirror. Calculate the object distance from the mirror and the magnification.

| *R.P. Convention* | *N.C. Convention* |
|---|---|
| Here $f = \dfrac{r}{2} = \dfrac{20}{2} = +10$ cm, | Here $f = \dfrac{r}{2} = \dfrac{-20}{2} = -10$ cm, |
| $v = -30$ cm (virtual image) | $v = +30$ cm (virtual image) |
| Substituting in $\dfrac{1}{v} + \dfrac{1}{u} = \dfrac{1}{f}$ , | Substituting in $\dfrac{1}{v} + \dfrac{1}{u} = \dfrac{1}{f}$ , |
| $\therefore \quad \dfrac{1}{(-30)} + \dfrac{1}{u} = \dfrac{1}{(+10)}$ | $\therefore \quad \dfrac{1}{(+30)} + \dfrac{1}{u} = \dfrac{1}{(-10)}$ |
| $\therefore \quad -\dfrac{1}{30} + \dfrac{1}{u} = \dfrac{1}{10}$ | $\therefore \quad \dfrac{1}{30} + \dfrac{1}{u} = -\dfrac{1}{10}$ |
| $\therefore \dfrac{1}{u} = \dfrac{1}{10} + \dfrac{1}{30} = \dfrac{4}{30}$ | $\therefore \dfrac{1}{u} = -\dfrac{1}{10} - \dfrac{1}{30} = -\dfrac{4}{30}$ |
| $\therefore u = \dfrac{30}{4} = 7.5$ cm | $\therefore u = -\dfrac{30}{4} = -7.5$ cm |
| $\therefore$ object is 7·5 cm in front of mirror | $\therefore$ object is 7·5 cm in front of mirror |
| *Magnification.* | *Magnification.* |
| $m = \dfrac{v}{u} = \dfrac{30}{7.5} = 4$ | $m = \dfrac{v}{u} = \dfrac{30}{7.5} = 4$ |

**2.** A convex mirror has a focal length of 20 cm. An image is produced which is two-thirds of the length of the object. *By drawing,* determine the object distance from the mirror. Verify by calculation.

*Drawing.*   Draw the principal axis DC and mark on it to scale the distance from the mirror, PB, of F, the principal focus, and C, the centre of curvature. Fig. 100A. Next, draw a line AB parallel and above DC, and a similar line LM which is two-thirds of the height of AB above DC.

Join FB, cutting LM produced at X. Now join CX and produce to cut BA at Y. Then OY is the object and XI is the image. Measure OP—this is the object distance from the mirror.

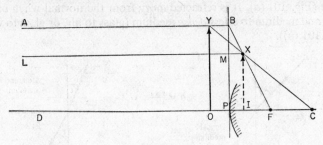

Fig. 100A. Drawing

*Calculation.*

| Real is Positive | New Cartesian |
|---|---|

Let $x$ cm = object distance, $u$.

Since $m = 2/3$,

$\therefore -2x/3$ cm
= image (virtual) distance, $v$

Also,

$$f = -20 \text{ cm (convex)}$$

Substituting in $\dfrac{1}{v} + \dfrac{1}{u} = \dfrac{1}{f}$,

$$\therefore \frac{1}{(-2x/3)} + \frac{1}{(+x)} = \frac{1}{(-20)}$$

$$\therefore -\frac{3}{2x} + \frac{1}{x} = -\frac{1}{20}$$

$$\therefore -\frac{1}{2x} = -\frac{1}{20}$$

$$\therefore x = 10 \text{ cm}$$

Let $-x$ cm = object distance, $u$.

Since $m = 2/3$,

$\therefore +2x/3$ cm
= image (virtual) distance, $v$

Also,

$$f = +20 \text{ cm (convex)}$$

Substituting in $\dfrac{1}{v} + \dfrac{1}{u} = \dfrac{1}{f}$,

$$\therefore \frac{1}{(+2x/3)} + \frac{1}{(-x)} = \frac{1}{(+20)}$$

$$\therefore \frac{3}{2x} - \frac{1}{x} = \frac{1}{20}$$

$$\therefore \frac{1}{2x} = \frac{1}{20}$$

$$\therefore x = 10 \text{ cm}$$

# REFRACTION AT PLANE SURFACES

*Refraction* is due to the change in velocity of light as it travels from one medium such as air to a different medium such as glass (p. 93).

*Laws of Refraction.*    1. The incident ray, refracted ray, and normal at the point of incidence all lie on the same plane.

2. The ratio *sin i/sin r is a constant* for two given media, where *i* is the angle of incidence in one medium and *r* is the angle of refraction in the second medium (Snell's law).

Remember that a light ray is refracted *towards* the normal when it passes from one medium to a *denser* medium (air to glass, or water to glass) (Fig. 101 (*a*)). It is refracted *away* from the normal when passing from one medium to a *less dense* medium (glass to air, or glass to water) (Fig. 101 (*b*)).

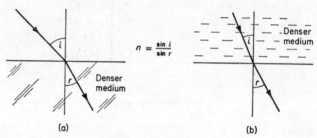

$$n = \frac{\sin i}{\sin r}$$

(a)                                                    (b)

FIG. 101. Refraction

*Refractive Index.*   Definition: This is the ratio sin $i$/sin $r$, where $i$ is the angle of incidence in one medium and $r$ is the angle of refraction in the other medium. If air–glass $n$ (refractive index) = 1·5, then glass–air $n = 1/1·5 = 2/3$, or less than 1.

*Refracted Rays.   Drawing method.* Consider refraction from air to water, $n = 4/3$. Draw two circles, one of radius 1 unit and the other of

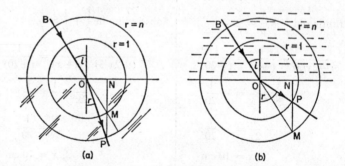

(a)                                                    (b)

FIG. 102. Drawing of refracted ray

radius $n$ units, with centre O (Fig. 102 (*a*)). Draw the incident ray BO at the angle of incidence $i$. Now produce BO to cut the smaller circle at M, and draw the line MN perpendicular to the boundary to cut the larger circle at P. Join OP. This is the refracted ray.

Fig. 102 (*b*) shows the drawing from a dense (e.g. water) to less dense medium (e.g. air). This time BO is produced to cut the *larger* circle at M, after which MN is drawn to cut the smaller circle at P. Then OP is the ray refracted away from the normal.

*Calculation.* Suppose the angle of incidence *i* on an *air–water* boundary is 60°. Then, if $n = 4/3$, the angle of refraction *r* is given by

$$\frac{\sin 60°}{\sin r} = n = \frac{4}{3}$$

$$\therefore \sin r = \frac{3}{4} \sin 60° = 0\!\cdot\!6498$$

$$\therefore r = 41° \text{ (approx.)}$$

If the angle of incidence on a *glass–air* boundary is 30° and *n* from air to glass is 1·5, then since *n* from glass to air is 1/1·5,

$$\frac{\sin 30°}{\sin r} = \frac{1}{1\cdot5}$$

$$\therefore \sin r = 1\!\cdot\!5 \sin 30° = 0\!\cdot\!75$$

$$\therefore \quad r = 49° \text{ (approx.)}$$

*Refractive Index Measurement.*  1. *Rectangular glass block* (Fig. 103 (*a*)). Use a ray-box X or pins. Choose a convenient angle of incidence such

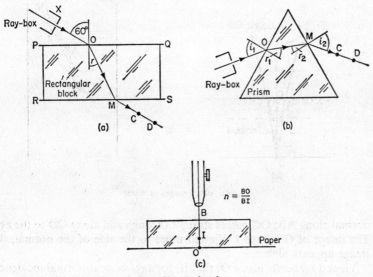

Fɪɢ. 103. Refraction

as 60°. Mark the boundaries PQ, RS on paper, mark two points C, D on the emerging ray, and produce CD to meet RS at M. *Join M to O to obtain the refracted ray OM.* Calculate *n* from sin *i*/sin *r*. Repeat with other angles of *i* and *r*.

2. *Glass prism.* Follow the same method (Fig. 103 (*b*)), that is,

join O and M to obtain the refracted ray in the glass. One ray, OMCD, provides two angles of incidence, $i_1$, $i_2$, and two angles of refraction, $r_1$, $r_2$.

3. *Apparent depth.* Unlike previous methods, this is an accurate method because measurements can be made with high precision. To find the refractive index of glass, focus a microscope on a pencil or ink mark O on paper; then place a glass block on it and re-focus onto the image I; and finally sprinkle chalk-dust on the top at B and re-focus again (Fig. 103 (*c*)). Calculation:

$$n = \frac{\text{true depth of glass}}{\text{apparent depth}} = \frac{OB}{IB}$$

To find the refractive index of water by the same method, use a small beaker of water with a pin at the bottom as an object.

*Apparent Depth.* A pool of water looks shallower viewed directly from above. To illustrate, take two or more rays (never one ray) from a point O below water (Fig. 104 (*a*)). OA is refracted *away* from the

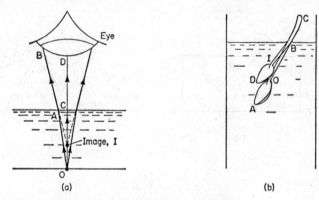

FIG. 104. Images in water

normal along AB; OC passes straight through and along CD to the eye. The image of O is thus I. Viewed more to the side of the normal, the image appears higher.

Viewed *vertically above* O, that is, for rays of near-normal incidence,

$$\frac{\text{true depth (OC)}}{\text{apparent depth (IC)}} = n$$

A pool of water, $n = 4/3$, 2 metres deep would appear to have a depth of

$$\frac{2 \text{ metres}}{4/3} = 1\tfrac{1}{2} \text{ metres}$$

*Partial-immersion.* A stick or spoon, ABC, partially immersed in water, looks 'bent' at the surface; it appears as DBC (Fig. 104 (ii)). A point O on the spoon is seen higher at I. Similarly for other points on AB. The images thus lie on DB.

*Total Internal Reflection.* Light travelling from *glass to air* at a small angle of incidence is partially-reflected at the boundary. The reflected light is weak. Most of the light is refracted *away* from the normal into air (Fig. 105 (*a*)).

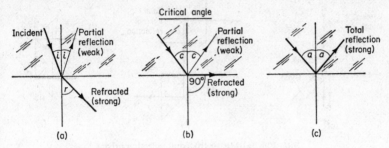

FIG. 105. Total internal reflection

When the angle of incidence is increased to a value *c* called the *critical angle*, the angle of refraction in air is 90° (Fig. 105 (*b*)). A weak reflected ray is still obtained. Beyond *c* no refraction occurs—the light is *totally reflected*. Thus: (1) Total internal reflection occurs only when light travels from an optically dense medium to a less dense medium (glass to air, or water to air)—never the reverse.

(2) The critical angle, *c*, is the angle of incidence in the dense medium when the angle of refraction in the less dense medium is 90°.

*Calculation of c.* For air–glass, *n* is 1·5 for crown glass. Hence for glass–air, *n* is 1/1·5.

$$\therefore \frac{\sin c}{\sin 90°} = \frac{1}{1·5}$$

$$\therefore \quad \sin c = \frac{1}{1·5} = \frac{2}{3} = 0·6667$$

$$\therefore c = 42° \text{ (approx.)}$$

For air–water, *n* is 4/3. Hence for water–air, *n* is 3/4.

$$\therefore \frac{\sin c}{\sin 90°} = \frac{3}{4}$$

$$\therefore \quad \sin c = \frac{3}{4} = 0·75$$

$$\therefore c = 49° \text{ (approx.)}$$

*Multiple Images*

*Total-reflecting Prisms.*    Mirrors silvered on the back of glass produce several images of an object O; this is due to reflection-refraction from air to glass (Fig. 106 (*a*)). Hence the image of O can not be focused with precision if mirrors are used in an optical instrument.

Total-reflecting prisms produce *one* bright image by reflection. Their angles are 90°, 45°, 45° and they are made of crown glass, $n = 1.5$

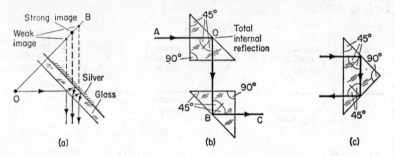

FIG. 106. (a) Mirror (b) Total reflecting prisms

(Fig. 106 (*b*)). The glass–air critical angle is about 42°. When a ray AO enters the glass side normally and is incident at O, the angle of incidence is 45° here, which is greater than 42°. *Total* internal reflection hence occurs. At B at the lower prism, the angle of incidence in the glass is 45° again. Hence total internal reflection occurs. The light is reflected along BC parallel to AO.

Fig. 106 (*b*) shows deviation of 90° by a prism, or the periscope principle. For deviation of 180°, or reversal of light path, the prism is turned as in Fig. 106 (*c*).

# LENSES

A convex or *converging lens* converges beams of light; it is thicker in the middle than at the edges (Fig. 107 (*a*)). A concave or *diverging lens*

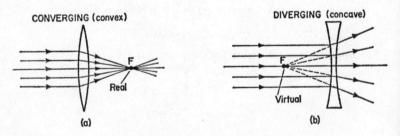

FIG. 107. Lenses and parallel rays

diverges beams of light; it is thinner in the middle than at the edges (Fig. 107 (*b*)).

*Definitions.* The *principal focus of a converging lens* is the point on the principal axis to which rays parallel and close to the principal axis converge after refraction through the lens. The principal focus, F, is *real* (Fig. 107 (*a*)).

The *principal focus of a diverging lens* is the point on the principal axis from which rays parallel and close to the principal axis appear to diverge after refraction through the lens. The principal focus, F, is virtual (Fig. 107 (*b*)).

The *focal length* of a lens is the distance from the principal focus to the lens.

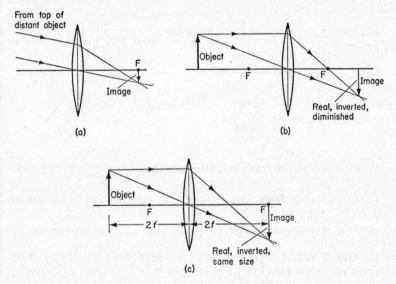

FIG. 108. Images in converging lens

The *optical centre* of a lens is the point in the principal axis between its surfaces such that rays refracted to pass through this point emerge undeviated. See Fig. 108.

The *transverse* or *linear magnification* is the ratio
*height of image*/*height of object*.

### Drawing Images

With thin lenses, (i) represent the lens by a straight line, (ii) draw a ray from the top point of the object parallel to the axis—this passes through the principal focus, (ii) draw a ray from the top point to the middle of the lens—this passes straight through undeviated. The two emerging rays pass through the top point of the image. See Fig. 108.

Note carefully that lines produced back from emerging rays to form a *virtual* image are represented by broken lines without arrows on them, as in Fig. 107 (*b*).

*Converging Lens Images.* (1) Object a long way from lens or 'at infinity'—image is at focus F of lens and is real, inverted, diminished. To show the formation of a sizeable image, draw parallel rays *at an angle* to the principal axis from the top point of the distance object (Fig. 108 (*a*)).

(2) Object farther than 2*f* from lens—image real, inverted, *diminished* (Fig. 108 (*b*)).

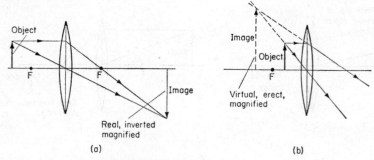

FIG. 109. Magnified images

(3) Object at 2*f* from lens—image real, inverted and *same size as object* (Fig. 108 (*c*)).

(4) Object between 2*f* and *f*—image real, inverted and *magnified* (Fig. 109 (*a*)).

(5) Object nearer than *f* to lens—image *virtual, erect, magnified*. (Magnifying glass principle.) Fig. 109 (*b*).

Summarizing: the image is real and inverted when the object is farther than *f* from the lens. Nearer than *f* it becomes virtual and erect.

*Diverging Lens Images.* The image is always *virtual, erect, diminished* (Fig. 110). Note carefully that a parallel ray appears to diverge from F, which is on the same side as the object. Do *not* confuse the position of F in relation to the lens. Compared with Fig. 109 (*b*), the virtual image is nearer to the lens than the object and is smaller.

*Examples.* 1. A converging lens has a focal length of 10 cm. By drawing, find the object distance when the image obtained is half its height.

Represent the lens position by AB (Fig. 111 (*a*)). Let CF = 10 cm to scale. Draw a line PQ parallel to the principal axis to cut CA at Q. Draw a line

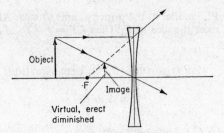

FIG. 110. Diverging lens image

GH parallel to the axes, where CG = ½QC. Join QF and let it cut GH at D. Join DC and produce to meet PQ at E. Draw EO perpendicular to the axis—this represents the object. ID represents the image. Measure OC and find the distance if CF represents 10 cm. OC = $u$ = 30 cm.

2. A magnifying glass produces an image four times the size of the object and is 20 cm from the lens. By drawing, determine the focal length of the lens.

Draw AB to represent the lens of centre C (Fig. 111 (b)). Draw the image IQ at a distance CI of 20 cm from the lens to scale. Draw the object OP one-quarter of the height of IQ to scale at a distance CO of 20/4 or 5 cm. Then QP passes through C.

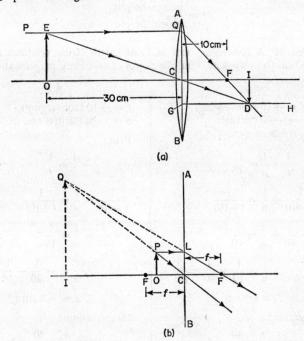

FIG. 111. Drawing of images

From P draw PL parallel to the principal axis to meet **AB** at L. Join QL and produce to meet the axis at F. Then CF $= f =$ focal length $= 6\cdot7$ cm by scale drawing.

*Lens Formulae.*   *Real is positive* (*R.P.*). Lens equation:

$$\frac{1}{v} + \frac{1}{u} = \frac{1}{f}$$

*New Cartesian* (*N.C.*). Lens equation:

$$\frac{1}{v} - \frac{1}{u} = \frac{1}{f}$$

In both conventions,

focal length $f$ is $+$ for converging (convex) lens

and

focal length $f$ is $-$ for diverging (concave) lens

Transverse or linear magnification:

$$m = \frac{\text{image height}}{\text{object height}} = \frac{v}{u}$$

*Examples.*   1. A converging lens of focal length 10 cm produces an erect image 40 cm from the lens. Find the object distance and magnification.

|  *R.P.*  |  *N.C.*  |
|---|---|

*R.P.*

$f = +10$ (converging)
$v = -40$ (virtual)

From

$$\frac{1}{v} + \frac{1}{u} = \frac{1}{f},$$

$$\therefore \frac{1}{(-40)} + \frac{1}{u} = \frac{1}{(+10)}$$

$$\therefore -\frac{1}{40} + \frac{1}{u} = \frac{1}{10}$$

$$\therefore \frac{1}{u} = \frac{1}{10} + \frac{1}{40} = \frac{5}{40}$$

$$\therefore u = 8 \text{ cm}$$

Magnification:

$$m = \frac{v}{u} = \frac{40}{8} = 5$$

*N.C.*

$f = +10$ (converging)
$v = -40$ (virtual and left of lens)

From

$$\frac{1}{v} - \frac{1}{u} = \frac{1}{f}$$

$$\therefore \frac{1}{(-40)} - \frac{1}{u} = \frac{1}{(+10)}$$

$$\therefore -\frac{1}{40} - \frac{1}{u} = \frac{1}{10}$$

$$\therefore \frac{1}{u} = -\frac{1}{40} - \frac{1}{10} = -\frac{5}{40}$$

$$\therefore u = -8 \text{ cm}$$

Magnification:

$$m = \frac{v}{u} = \frac{40}{8} = 5$$

2. The image in a diverging lens is 12 cm from the lens. If the magnification is one-half, find the focal length.

|  R.P.  |  N.C.  |
|---|---|

R.P.

$v = -12$ cm (virtual)
∴ $u = 2 \times 12 = +24$ cm (real)

From

$$\frac{1}{v} + \frac{1}{u} = \frac{1}{f}$$

$$\therefore \frac{1}{(-12)} + \frac{1}{(+24)} = \frac{1}{f}$$

$$\therefore \quad -\frac{1}{12} + \frac{1}{24} = \frac{1}{f}$$

$$\therefore \quad -\frac{1}{24} = \frac{1}{f}$$

$$\therefore f = -24 \text{ cm}$$

N.C.

$v = -12$ cm (left of lens)
∴ $u = 2 \times 12 = -24$ cm
(left of lens)

From

$$\frac{1}{v} - \frac{1}{u} = \frac{1}{f}$$

$$\therefore \frac{1}{(-12)} - \frac{1}{(-24)} = \frac{1}{f}$$

$$\therefore \quad -\frac{1}{12} + \frac{1}{24} = \frac{1}{f}$$

$$\therefore \quad -\frac{1}{24} = \frac{1}{f}$$

$$\therefore f = -24 \text{ cm}$$

3. A converging lens produces an erect image four times the object height. If the focal length is 20 cm, find the object distance.

R.P.

Let $u = x$ cm

Then $v = -4x$ cm (virtual)

From

$$\frac{1}{v} + \frac{1}{u} = \frac{1}{f}$$

$$\therefore \frac{1}{(-4x)} + \frac{1}{(+x)} = \frac{1}{(+20)}$$

$$\therefore \quad -\frac{1}{4x} + \frac{1}{x} = \frac{1}{20}$$

$$\therefore \frac{3}{4x} = \frac{1}{20}$$

$$\therefore x = 15$$

$$\therefore u = 15 \text{ cm}$$

N.C.

Let $u = -x$ cm (left of lens)

Then $v = -4x$ (left of lens)

From

$$\frac{1}{v} - \frac{1}{u} = \frac{1}{f}$$

$$\therefore \frac{1}{(-4x)} - \frac{1}{(-x)} = \frac{1}{(+20)}$$

$$\therefore \quad -\frac{1}{4x} + \frac{1}{x} = \frac{1}{20}$$

$$\therefore \frac{3}{4x} = \frac{1}{20}$$

$$\therefore x = 15$$

$$\therefore u = -15 \text{ cm}$$

## Focal Length Measurements

*Converging Lens.* 1. *Plane mirror.* Place a plane mirror M behind the lens L (Fig. 112 (a)). Move an illuminated object O (e.g. crosswires) until a *clear* image I is formed beside O. Measure OL. Then OL = f.

Explanation: When I formed beside O, rays are all incident normally

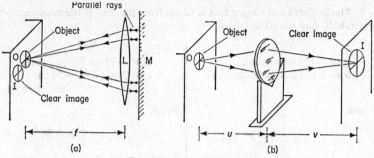

FIG. 112. Measurement of *f*

on M; so a *parallel beam* is reflected from M to L and this converges to the focus.

2. *Object and image*. Obtain a clear image I of an illuminated object O on a screen (Fig. 112 (*b*)). Measure *u* and *v*. Substitute in the lens formula and calculate *f*.

3. *Quick but not accurate*. Project a clear image of the window frame at the back of a room on to paper, and measure the distance from the image to the paper. Since, approximately, parallel rays come from an object a long way off, this distance is the focal length.

## OPTICAL INSTRUMENTS

### *Lens Camera*

This should be compared and contrasted with the eye (p. 129). It has (1) a *converging (convex) lens*, (2) a *diaphragm* or *stop*, which limits the light passing through to the central part of the lens so that the image formed is a clear one (light on the outer part of the lens is not brought to the same focus as that on the central part), (3) a *light-sensitive film* on which the real inverted image is formed (Fig. 113).

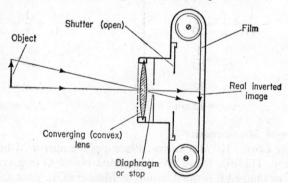

FIG. 113. Lens camera

An object is focused by moving the lens. The amount of light entering the lens is controlled by the diameter of the diaphragm or stop and by the speed of the shutter, which is pre-set for the particular lighting conditions.

### Simple Microscope

The simple microscope (magnifying glass) also consists of a converging lens of short focal length, like the lens camera. But this time (i) the object is nearer the lens than its focal length (in the camera it is farther from the lens than its focal length), (ii) the image is viewed directly by the eye and is erect and virtual (in the camera it is real, inverted and small and formed on a light-sensitive film). See Fig. 109 (b).

### Compound Microscope

This produces a much greater magnification than the simple microscope. It has an objective and eyepiece which are both converging and of short focal length (e.g. a few centimetres) (Fig. 114). The object A is placed just beyond the principal focus, $F_0$, of the objective. The

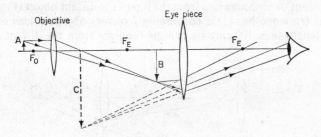

FIG. 114. Compound microscope

latter forms a magnified image B. The eyepiece is used as a simple magnifying glass to increase the magnification further, so that a large inverted image is seen at C. Note carefully that *the rays from A through the top point of B are continued to meet the eyepiece*, which refracts them to enter the eye.

### Projection Lantern

This has (i) a powerful small source of light O, (ii) a condensing lens to collect the light from O and send it through the slide S which is then illuminated powerfully, (iii) a converging projection lens L, (iv) a distant white screen A (Fig. 115). Unlike the compound microscope, the object S is slightly farther from L than its focal length, so that a real large inverted image is obtained on the screen. The linear magnification, $m$, is $v/u$; each side of the slide is magnified $v/u$ times. In contrast to a compound microscope, the final large image is formed on a screen

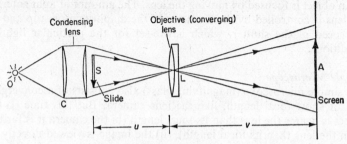

FIG. 115. Projection lantern (*not to scale*)

and then observed, whereas in a microscope the final large image is virtual and seen directly by the eye-lens.

### Astronomical Telescope

A telescope is used for viewing distant objects. Thus *parallel rays, inclined at a small angle to the principal axis,* are always drawn arriving at the front or objective lens from the top of the distant object (Fig. 116).

This telescope has (1) a converging (convex) objective lens of long focal length (e.g. 100 cm)—it collects the light from the distant object

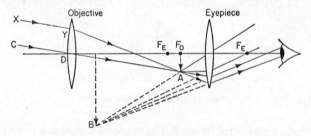

FIG. 116. Astronomical telescope

and brings it to its focus, $F_0$, (2) a converging eyepiece lens of short focal length (e.g. 4 cm)—it magnifies the image due to the objective, as in the magnifying glass (p. 122).

To draw the final image, first construct the image A of the distant object in the objective—draw the central ray CD first, producing it to a point below $F_0$ to obtain the head of the inverted image. Next, construct the image B of A in the eyepiece as on p. 127; but do *not* place any arrows on the lines used as they are construction lines only. Now produce the actual rays YA and DA to meet the eyepiece lens and join them back to the top point of B. Then produce the lines forward through the eyepiece lens to represent actual rays, which emerge from the eyepiece and enter the eye.

Observe that (a) the final image is inverted, (b) the distance apart of the two lenses is just less than the sum of their focal lengths. Two converging lenses of 80 cm and 5 cm focal length will thus act as an astronomical telescope if their distance apart is about 85 cm.

### Galilean Telescope (Opera Glass)

This produces an erect final image. It has (1) a converging or convex objective of long focal length, (2) a *diverging* or *concave* eyepiece of

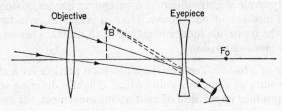

FIG. 117. Galilean telescope

short focal length. The distance apart of the lenses is the *difference* in the focal lengths (approx.) (Fig. 117).

Unlike the astronomical telescope, the beam refracted through the objective is incident on the concave lens *before* reaching the focus. *The eyepiece is moved so that a diverging beam emerges*, as shown in Fig. 117, and a virtual erect final image is now formed at B.

## THE EYE, DEFECTS OF VISION

### Structure of Eye

The eye has: (1) crystalline flexible lens L—it is converging and surrounded by liquids (aqueous and vitreous humours, A.H. and V.H.); (2)

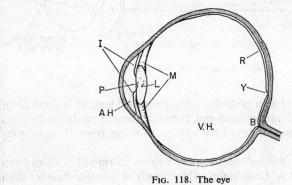

FIG. 118. The eye

iris, I—coloured and surrounding L; (3) pupil, P—hole in middle of iris, contracting by day and widening at night to control amount of light passing through; (4) ciliary muscles, M—surrounds lens and controls focal length by altering radii of curvature of surfaces; (5) retina, R—light-sensitive layer of cells at rear of eye; (6) fovea-centralis or yellow spot, Y—most sensitive part of retina; (7) blind spot, B—on optic nerve and insensitive to light (Fig. 118).

### Binocular Vision

Two eyes provide slightly different overlapping images, giving sense of depth and distance or perspective. Hunted creatures have two eyes in the head which provide independent views all round, whereas beasts of prey have binocular vision.

*Persistence of Vision.* The sensation of vision persists for a short time after the source of light has switched off. Slightly differing scenes can therefore produce impression of continuous movement, for example, in cinema films.

*Defects of Vision.* 1. *Short sight.* Normal vision—objects a long way off, 'at infinity', can be clearly seen. With short sight, due to long eye-ball, only objects at a shorter distance such as at P can be clearly seen (Fig. 119 (*a*)).

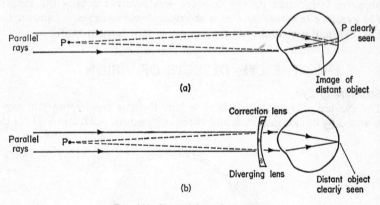

FIG. 119. Short sight and correction

Correction—use a suitable diverging (concave) lens. If farthest point distinctly seen is 2 metres from eye, then focal length needed is 2 metres (Fig. 119 (*b*)). Parallel rays now appear to come from P *on entering the eye.*

2. *Long sight.* Normal vision—near objects 25 cm (10 in.) away can be clearly seen at A. Long sight—objects only at a longer distance than

25 cm, at Q, can be seen owing to a short eyeball, for example (Fig. 120 (a)).

Correction—use a suitable converging (convex) lens. Rays from A now appear to come from Q *on entering the eye* (Fig. 120 (ii)).

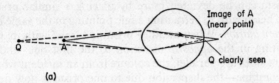

(a)

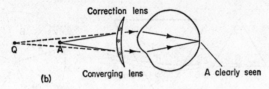

(b)

FIG. 120. Far sight and correction

## COLOURS AND SPECTRA

### Dispersion by Prism

*Dispersion* is the separation of colours from a mixture. A parallel-sided glass block disperses the colours in white light only slightly. A glass prism of 60° angle disperses the colours considerably. Fig. 121.

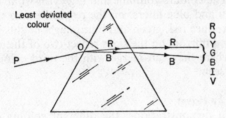

FIG. 121. Dispersion

The spectrum (colours) of white light are:

Red, Orange, Yellow, Green, Blue, Indigo, Violet (R O Y G B I V)

A ray of white light PO is dispersed at O by the first face of the prism into its various colours (Fig. 121). The coloured rays are then refracted *without further colour change* at the second face but the amount of dispersion is increased. The emerging light is deviated towards the base of the prism.

Dispersion is due to the different speeds in glass of the various colours;

in empty space or air they all travel at the same speed. *Red is deviated least* by refraction and blue is deviated most (Fig. 121). The refractive index of glass for blue light is hence greater than that for red.

*Effect of Prisms on Colours.* 1. *Further deviation.* Colours emerging from a prism can be deviated more by placing a similar prism in the path of the beam with its refracting angle pointing in the same direction.

2. *Re-combination.* When another prism is turned with its refracting angle pointing in the *opposite* direction to the first one, and the two facing prism sides are parallel, the colours from an incident white ray W tend to recombine—the dispersion due to one prism is now neutralized by the other (Fig. 122 (*a*)).

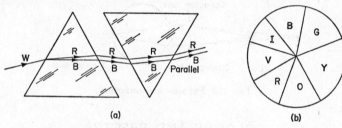

(a)                                    (b)

Fig. 122. Combining colours

### Adding Colours and Coloured Lights

1. Rotate a circular disc (Newton colour disc) having the different colours red, orange, yellow, green, blue and violet painted in sectors (Fig. 122 (*b*)). The colours combine and a greyish-white colour is seen.

2. Red, green and blue filters, on the respective two sides and front of a ray-box, produce red, green and blue images of slits illuminated by the lamp. Hinged mirrors on the sides reflect two of the colours on to a white screen, where they can merge with the third colour. An impure white image is seen.

### Pure Spectrum by Prism

In simple prism demonstrations, the different colours of white light overlap and only the edges are coloured distinctly. This is an *impure* spectrum.

A *pure spectrum* is one in which each part has only one colour. A narrow illuminated slit and parallel beams are needed to produce a pure spectrum. Fig. 123 (*a*) shows (i) source of white light, S, (ii) a narrow slit, (iii) a lens, C, with the slit at its focus, (iii) a 60° prism, P, (iv) a lens, T, (v) a white screen, A, at the focus of T.

The lens C produces a white parallel beam. Each incident ray such as W is dispersed into colours such as red R and blue B. Inside the prism, all the red colours are parallel and all the blue colours are parallel but in a different direction. The colours are collected by the lens T and brought to *different* foci at R and B, for example. A pure spectrum (no overlapping) is then obtained.

With only *one* prism (Fig. 123 (*b*)), an image of the slit H is first

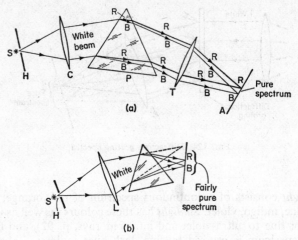

(a)

(b)

FIG. 123. Pure Spectrum

projected on a white screen (not shown) by the converging lens L. The prism is then placed to intercept the beam, and the screen is moved round until colours are seen. The prism is then turned until the least deviation of the colours is obtained, when the spectrum is fairly pure.

### Spectra by Diffraction Grating

A diffraction grating (p. 94) produces a spectrum. Holding a grating of a few thousand lines per cm close to the eye and viewing a source of white light such as an electric lamp, a number of coloured images are seen in addition to a central fairly white image. Each image has *blue* on the side nearest to the central image, showing this colour is least deviated.

To demonstrate a pure spectrum of white light, replace the prism in Fig. 123 (*a*) by a grating positioned normally to the incident white light (Fig. 124). Observe that:

(1) The colours are separated in a prism because their velocity in glass is different, whereas the separation by a grating is due to interference of waves (see p. 94).

(2) With a prism, red is the colour least deviated from the incident direction—with a grating, blue, B, is the colour least deviated and red, R, is most deviated (Fig. 124).

(3) With a prism, only one image of the spectrum is formed, whereas with a grating several images of the spectrum may be formed in different directions.

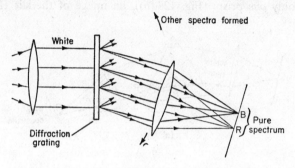

FIG. 124. Diffraction grating spectra

### Spectra

*White light* consists of a continuous spectrum of red, orange, yellow, green, blue, indigo, violet. *Sunlight* has these colours (as well as invisible radiations due to ultra-violet and infra-red rays, p. 92), and the continuous spectrum is crossed by fine dark lines indicating absorption spectra (see below). *Sodium vapour* has only two very close yellow lines; *mercury vapour* emits green and blue colours; *neon gas* emits an orange colour; and *hydrogen gas* emits all the different colours but as separated lines or as a 'line spectrum'.

*Absorption spectra* are dark lines in a spectrum due to absorption of wavelengths by a substance. The lines are characteristic of the absorber and are examples of 'optical resonance' (p. 98).

### Colours of Objects

A blue flower or a blue coat absorbs all the colours of the spectrum except blue, which it reflects. If it is illuminated in a dark room in turn by all the colours in the spectrum, it will appear black except in blue light, since it absorbs all other colours.

### Colours: Additive and Subtractive Colour Mixing

As shown with the aid of three lamps covered by red, blue and green filters respectively and shining on a white screen, a suitable mixture of these coloured lights can produce white light when added together. Red, blue and green are called *primary colours*.

The *complementary colour* of a primary colour is the colour which, subtracted from white light, produces that primary colour. It is also called a 'subtractive primary' colour. Complementary colours are: yellow—which gives blue when subtracted from white light; magenta—

which gives green when subtracted; and cyan—which gives red when subtracted.

Unlike primary colours, *secondary colours* are colours such as yellow which can be made by mixing two or more primary colours.

*Pigments* (*paints*) produce colours by a subtractive process. Blue paint absorbs all colours except blue and green; yellow paint absorbs all colours except yellow, orange and green. Mixed together, blue and yellow paints thus produce *green*.

# 7 Current Electricity

---

## ELECTRIC CIRCUITS

### Current (I)

This is the *quantity of electricity per second* flowing past a point. Hence $I = Q/t$, where $Q$ is the quantity of electricity flowing past in a time $t$.

$$1 \text{ ampere (A)} = 1 \text{ coulomb per second}$$

(i) In *metals*, the electricity is carried by electrons or negative charges; in *electrolytes*, it is carried by positive and negative ions; in *gases*, it is carried by electrons and ions; in *semiconductors*, it is carried by electrons and holes (equivalent to positive charges, $+e$, numerically equal to that on an electron).

(ii) Electron charge, $e = 1 \cdot 6 \times 10^{-19}$ coulomb. 1 ampere of current in a metal is hence due to the flow of about $1/1 \cdot 6 \times 10^{-19}$ or $6 \times 10^{18}$ electrons per second past a point.

(iii) An *ammeter* is a current measuring instrument; a *galvanometer* is a very sensitive detector or measurer of current. Instruments which measure current are always placed *in series* with the resistor concerned. They have low resistances.

### Potential Difference (V)

A potential difference (p.d.) is required to make a current flow. Potential difference is measured in volts (V). A quantity of electricity gains or loses energy when it moves between two points having a potential difference.

Definition: The p.d. between two points is numerically equal to the energy change in joules when 1 coulomb is transferred from one point to the other. Thus 1 volt is the p.d. when 1 joule of energy is released in transferring 1 coulomb between the points.

A *voltmeter* measures p.d. In contrast to the ammeter, it is always placed across, or *in parallel* with, the resistor concerned. Voltmeters should have high resistances compared with the resistor.

## Resistance (R)

Resistance, $$R = V/I$$

by definition, where $V$ is the p.d. and $I$ is the current flowing. Memorize:

$$I = V/R, \quad V = IR, \quad R = V/I$$

In the formula, $I$ is in amperes (A), $V$ in volts (V), $R$ in ohms ($\Omega$).

## Ohm's Law

Ohm's law states: The ratio of the potential difference $V$ across a conductor to the current $I$ flowing in it is always a constant, provided its physical conditions such as temperature are unaltered.

Manganin or eureka wire (resistance wire) obey Ohm's law (Fig.

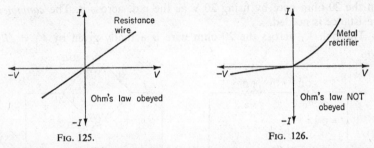

FIG. 125.   FIG. 126.

Ohmic and non-ohmic resistors

125). A metal rectifier (e.g. the junction of copper oxide–copper), or a junction diode (a semiconductor diode), or a radio diode valve, do *not* obey Ohm's law, since the $I$–$V$ graph is not a continuous straight line passing through the origin (Fig. 126).

## Measurement of Resistance

Fig. 127 shows a circuit for measuring resistance $R$ by using a voltmeter, V, and ammeter, A. The readings can be varied by altering the rheostat S. Then $R = V/I$, where $R$ is in ohms when $V$ is in volts and $I$ in amps.

*Series Resistors.* (i) The combined or total resistance $R$ of resistances $R_1$, $R_2$ in series is given by $R = R_1 + R_2$ (Fig. 128 (a)); (ii) *the same current, I, flows in both resistances.*

In Fig. 128 (a), the p.d. across *both* resistances is 20 V. Thus the current flowing, if $R$ is the combined resistance, is

$$I = \frac{V}{R} = \frac{20}{25} = 0.8 \text{ A}$$

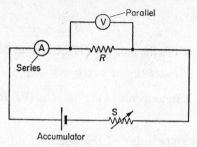

FIG. 127. Measurement of resistance

This is the current flowing in each wire. Note carefully that, because 20 V is the p.d. across both resistors, it is *wrong* to calculate the current in the 20-ohm wire by using 20 V as the p.d. across it. The *combined* resistance is needed.

The p.d. $V_1$ across the 20-ohm wire is actually given by $V_1 = IR_1$

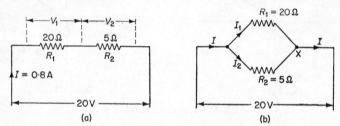

FIG. 128. Series and parallel resistors

$= 0.8 \times 20 = 16$ V. The p.d. $V_2$ across the 5-ohm wire is similarly given by $V_2 = IR_2 = 0.8 \times 5 = 4$ V. Observe that, as a check,

$$\text{total p.d.} = 16 \text{ V} + 4 \text{ V} = 20 \text{ V} = \text{p.d. applied}$$

Thus if the total p.d. applied to two wires in series is 6 V and the p.d. across one wire is 1 V, the p.d. across the second wire $= 6 - 1 = 5$ V.

*Parallel Resistors.* The combined or total resistance $R$ of resistances $R_1$, $R_2$ in parallel is given by

$$\frac{1}{R} = \frac{1}{R_1} + \frac{1}{R_2}$$

Thus, from Fig. 128 (*b*), the combined resistance $R$ is found from

$$\frac{1}{R} = \frac{1}{20} + \frac{1}{5} = \frac{5}{20} = \frac{1}{4}$$

Hence $R = 4$ ohms. The current $I$ flowing outside the two wires is therefore given by $I = V/R = 20/4 = 5$ A.

Unlike the series case, the p.d. across each wire is the same and equal to 20 V. In the 20-ohm wire, $R_1$, $I_1 = V/R_1 = 20/20 = 1$ A. In the 5-ohm wire, $R_2$, $I_2 = V/R_2 = 20/5 = 4$ A. Observe that $I_1 + I_2 = 1$ A $+ 4$ A $= 5$ A $= I$. This shows that no electricity accumulates at junctions of circuits such as X—the current or charges moving towards X from $R_1$, $R_2$ add together and form the current $I$.

*Proof of resistance formulae.* *Series.* We have $V = V_1 + V_2$, where $V$ is the applied p.d. and $V_1$, $V_2$ are the p.d.s across the individual resistances $R_1$, $R_2$. But $V_1 = IR_1$, $V_2 = IR_2$,

$$\therefore \qquad V = IR_1 + IR_2 = I(R_1 + R_2)$$

$$\therefore \text{ combined resistance } R = R_1 + R_2$$

*Parallel.* We have $I = I_1 + I_2$. But $I_1 = V/R_1$, $I_2 = V/R_2$,

$$\therefore I = \frac{V}{R_1} + \frac{V}{R_2} = V\left(\frac{1}{R_1} + \frac{1}{R_2}\right)$$

$$\therefore \frac{I}{V} = \frac{1}{R} = \frac{1}{R_1} + \frac{1}{R_2}$$

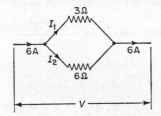

FIG. 129. Parallel resistors

*Currents in Parallel Resistors.* Suppose a current of 6 amp flows towards the junction of two wires of 3 and 6 ohms in parallel (Fig. 129). The current in each wire can always be calculated by first finding the p.d. $V$ across *both* resistors. Their total resistance, $R$, is given by

$$\frac{1}{R} = \frac{1}{3} + \frac{1}{6} = \frac{3}{6} \quad \text{or} \quad R = \frac{6}{3} = 2 \text{ ohms}$$

$$\therefore V = IR = 6 \times 2 = 12 \text{ V}$$

$$\therefore \text{ current, } I_1, \text{ in 3-ohm wire, } R_1 = \frac{V}{R_1} = \frac{12}{3} = 4 \text{ A}$$

and        current, $I_2$, in 6-ohm wire, $R_2 = \dfrac{V}{R_2} = \dfrac{12}{6} = 2$ A

As a check, $I_1 + I_2 = 4 + 2 = 6$ A.

5

Note that 6 amp is *not* the current in each wire but the current in the *combined* or total resistance, $R$.

The same method can be used to find the currents in each of three wires in parallel. Thus (i) find the combined or total resistance $R$, (ii) calculate the p.d. $V$ across all three wires from $V = IR$, (iii) use $I_1 = V/R_1$, etc., for each wire.

### Resistivity

*Definition.* The resistivity, $\rho$, of a material is the resistance of a unit length of unit cross-sectional area. Units of resistivity: ohm metre ($\Omega$ m).

The simplest shape of material with unit length and unit cross-sectional area is a cube.

Formula:
$$R = \frac{\rho l}{A}$$

where $R$ is the resistance of a length $l$ of cross-sectional area $A$. If $l$ is in m, $A$ in m$^2$ and $\rho$ in ohm m, then $R$ is in ohms.

*Example.* Find the length of wire required to make a 50-ohm coil from nichrome wire of resistivity 1 microhm metre and diameter 0·2 mm. We have

$$\rho = \frac{1}{10^6} \text{ ohm metre}, \quad A = \frac{\pi d^2}{4} = \frac{\pi \times (0\cdot2/1000)^2}{4} \text{ m}^2, \quad R = 50 \text{ ohms}$$

From
$$R = \frac{\rho l}{A}$$

$$\therefore l = \frac{R \cdot A}{\rho} = \frac{50 \times \pi \times 0\cdot2^2}{4 \times 1000^2/10^6} \text{ m}$$

$$= \frac{50 \times \pi \times 0\cdot04}{4} = 1\cdot57 \text{ m}$$

*Measurement of Resistivity.* Measure a suitable length $l$ of wire, such as 100 cm, with a metre rule. Measure the diameter $d$ in several places with a micrometer screw-gauge and take the average value.

Connect the wire in a suitable circuit and measure the resistance $R$ by a voltmeter-ammeter method. Calculate the resistivity $\rho$ from the relation $\rho = R \cdot A/l = R \cdot \pi d^2/4l$.

*Effect of Temperature.* 1. Pure metals, such as tungsten or copper, increase in resistance when their temperature rises.

2. Carbon, non-metals and semiconductors such as germanium and silicon decrease in resistance when their temperature rises.

3. Alloys such as Manganin and Constantan are practically unaffected by temperature change. *Resistance coils* are made of these materials as their resistance should keep constant as their temperature rises.

*Wheatstone Bridge. Metre Bridge.* An unknown resistance *P* can be measured with the *metre bridge* circuit in Fig. 130, using a known resistance *Q* of the same order of magnitude. At a balance-point D,

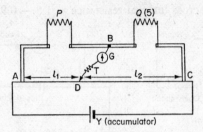

Fig. 130. Metre bridge (T=protective resistor for G)

i.e. no deflection in the sensitive galvanometer G, then, if $l_1$ = length AD and $l_2$ = length DC,

$$\frac{P}{Q} = \frac{l_1}{l_2} \quad \text{or} \quad P = Q \times \frac{l_1}{l_2}$$

Thus if $Q = 5{\cdot}0$ ohm, $l_1 = 56{\cdot}2$ cm, $l_2 = 43{\cdot}8$ cm, then $P = 5{\cdot}0 \times 56{\cdot}2/43{\cdot}8 = 6{\cdot}4$ ohm.

*Note.* The metre bridge is one form of a 'Wheatstone bridge' circuit. The latter uses a no-deflection or null method of measurement. This is much more accurate than the voltmeter-ammeter method of measuring resistance (p. 137) because pointer instruments have zero errors; whereas the Wheatstone bridge uses the galvanometer only as a current detecting (not measuring) instrument.

# E.M.F. AND INTERNAL RESISTANCE

### E.M.F. (E)
An electric battery or generator is a source of energy or power.

Definition: The electromotive force (e.m.f.), *E*, of a battery is the *total energy per coulomb* obtained from it, or the *total power per ampere*.

The e.m.f. maintains the current in the whole circuit, both outside and inside the battery or generator.

### Internal Resistance (r)
The internal resistance, *r*, is the resistance of the battery or generator while working.

*Circuits.* The e.m.f. *E* may also be defined as *the p.d. of a battery or generator on open circuit*, that is, it is the p.d. across the terminals when no resistance is connected. In Fig. 131 (*a*), the e.m.f. of the cell is 1·5 V.

When a resistance of 3 ohms is joined to the terminals, the cell is on *closed circuit*. The voltmeter now reads 0·9 V (Fig. 131 (*b*)). This is the p.d. across the *external* resistance, 3 ohms,

∴ p.d. across internal resistance = 1·5 − 0·9 = 0·6 V

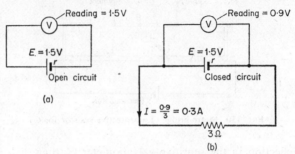

FIG. 131. E.m.f. and internal resistance

The current, $I$, $= V/R = 0.9 \, V/3 \, \Omega = 0.3$ A. It flows in both the external and internal resistance because they are in series.

Generally, e.m.f. $E$ depends only on the nature of the chemicals used in the battery and not on their amount. Internal resistance $r$ depends on the amount of chemicals used and on their condition. Always take $E$ and $r$ as constant values in calculations unless otherwise stated.

*Formulae.* The e.m.f. $E$ is the p.d. across both the external and internal resistance. If $R$ is the total external resistance and $r$ is the internal resistance, then

$$I = \frac{E}{R + r}$$

When a current flows, the p.d. $V$ at the terminals is always the p.d. across the *external* resistance $R$. Thus $I = V/R$. Since $(E - V) =$ p.d. across *internal* resistance, $r$, then

$$I = (E - V)/r$$

*Examples.* 1. A battery has an e.m.f. of 12 V and internal resistance of 2 ohms. (i) What current flows when a resistor of 8 ohms is connected to it, (ii) what is the p.d. across the terminals?

(i) $$I = \frac{E}{R + r} = \frac{12}{2 + 8} = 1.2 \text{ A.}$$

(ii) P.D. across terminals = p.d. across 8-ohm wire = $IR = 1.2 \times 8 = 9.6$ V.

2. A resistor of 6-ohms is joined to a battery of e.m.f. 20 V. If the p.d. at the terminals is 12 V, calculate the internal resistance of the battery.

What is the current flowing from the battery when another wire of 6-ohms is joined to it?

(i) Current flowing,

$$I = \frac{12}{6} = 2 \text{ A}$$

since 12 V (*not* 20 V) is the p.d. across the external resistance of 6 ohms. Now

p.d. across internal resistance = e.m.f. − p.d. across 6-ohm wire
$$= 20 - 12 = 8 \text{ V}$$

$\therefore$ internal resistance, $r = \dfrac{\text{p.d.}}{\text{current}} = \dfrac{8}{2} = 4 \text{ ohm}$

(ii) When another 6-ohm is joined in parallel, the combined resistance $R$ with the 6-ohm present is given by

$$\frac{1}{R} = \frac{1}{6} + \frac{1}{6} = \frac{1}{3} \quad \text{or} \quad R = 3 \text{ ohms}$$

$\therefore$ current, $I = \dfrac{E}{R + r} = \dfrac{20}{3 + 4} = 2\frac{6}{7} \text{ A}$

*Internal Resistance Investigation.* Join a voltmeter to the cell on open circuit and observe the e.m.f. $E$. Now connect a resistance of a few ohms and observe the new reading $V$ on the voltmeter. If it is practically the same as before, then very little p.d. is needed to drive the current through the internal resistance, $r$. Hence $r$ is very low, as for an acid accumulator. If $V$ falls appreciably, then $r$ is appreciable.

To measure $r$, include a suitable ammeter in the circuit and measure the current $I$ when the circuit is made. Then

$$r = \frac{\text{p.d.}}{\text{current}} = \frac{E - V}{I}.$$

### Cells in Series and Parallel
*Series.* If two cells, of e.m.f.s $E_1$, $E_2$ and internal resistances $r_1$, $r_2$ respectively, assist each other, then

$$\text{total e.m.f.} = E_1 + E_2$$

$$\text{total internal resistance} = r_1 + r_2$$

Thus if two assisting cells have e.m.f.s of 2 V and 6 V and internal resistances of 3 and 8 ohms respectively, the current flowing when a resistor of 9 ohms is connected to them is given by

$$I = \frac{2 + 6}{3 + 8 + 9} = \frac{8}{20} = 0.4 \text{ A}$$

If one of the cells is turned round, the e.m.f.s *oppose* each other. The total internal resistance, however, is unchanged. Hence new current, $I$, is given by

$$I = \frac{6 - 2}{3 + 8 + 9} = \frac{4}{20} = 0.2 \text{ A}$$

*Parallel.*   There is no general formula for the combined or total e.m.f. of different cells in parallel. If two *exactly* similar cells, for example two Leclanché cells, are in parallel with like poles joined together, then, if each cell has an e.m.f. of 1·5 V and internal resistance 2 ohms,

total e.m.f. = e.m.f. of *one* cell = 1·5 V

This is because the cells in parallel are equivalent to one larger similar cell, whose e.m.f. is the same as each individual cell.

The combined internal resistance, $r$, however, is that of two resistances, each 2 ohms, in parallel. Hence $1/r = 1/2 + 1/2 = 1$, or $r = 1$ ohm.

*Example.*   Two batteries, each of e.m.f. 3 V and internal resistance 4 ohms, are joined (i) in series, and then (ii) in parallel. Calculate the current through each cell if a wire of 2 ohms is joined to each arrangement.

(i) *Series.*

Total e.m.f., $E = 3 + 3 = 6$ V

Total internal resistance, $r = 4 + 4 = 8$ ohm

$$\therefore \text{ current, } I = \frac{6}{8 + 2} = \frac{6}{10} = 0.6 \text{ A} \qquad \ldots(i)$$

(ii) *Parallel.*

Total e.m.f. $E = 3$ V

Total internal resistance, $r$, is given by

$$\frac{1}{r} = \frac{1}{4} + \frac{1}{4} = \frac{1}{2} \quad \text{or} \quad r = 2 \text{ ohms}$$

$$\therefore \text{ current, } I = \frac{3}{2 + 2} = \tfrac{3}{4} \text{ A} \qquad \ldots(ii)$$

In the series case, the current of 0·6 A flows through each battery. In the parallel case, *half* the current of 3 A/4 flows through each battery as the current divides between the two. Hence the current through each = 3 A/8.

## Potentiometer

*Comparison of e.m.f.s.*   Accurate measurement of e.m.f. or p.d. is done with a *potentiometer*. This consists of a resistance wire BO 100 cm long, with an accumulator A connected to it to maintain a constant current.

To compare e.m.f.s, one cell C is connected as shown in Fig. 132. Its positive pole is joined to the same terminal B as that of the positive pole of the accumulator A; and its negative pole is joined through a sensitive centre-zero galvanometer G to a jockey or slider which is moved along BO. When a balance-point M is obtained, the e.m.f. $E_1$ of C is exactly balanced by the *p.d.* $V_1$ *along the wire BM*. (No current

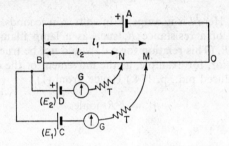

FIG. 132. Potentiometer

is now taken from C.) The length $l_1$ of BM is measured. Repeating with a cell of e.m.f. $E_2$, a balance-length $l_2$ or BN is obtained, Thus:

$$\frac{E_1}{E_2} = \frac{V_1}{V_2}$$

But, at balance, if $I$ is the constant current flowing from the accumulator through the wire, $V_1 = IR_1$ and $V_2 = IR_2$, where $R_1$, $R_2$ are the respective resistances of BM ($l_1$) and BN ($l_2$) of the wire,

$$\therefore \frac{E_1}{E_2} = \frac{IR_1}{IR_2} = \frac{R_1}{R_2} = \frac{l_1}{l_2}$$

Thus if $l_1 = 47.6$ cm, $l_2 = 52.4$ cm, then $E_1/E_2 = 47.6/52.4 = 0.91$. A 'standard' cell, one whose e.m.f. $E_2$, say, is accurately known, enables an unknown e.m.f. $E_1$ to be found by comparison, using a potentiometer.

Note that a moving-coil voltmeter connected to a cell takes a small current from the cell, and hence the reading of p.d. is not accurately the e.m.f. (the p.d. on open circuit). In the potentiometer method no current is taken from the cell at a balance; and hence the terminal p.d. measured is accurately the e.m.f.

# ELECTRICAL ENERGY AND POWER.
# HEATING EFFECT

### Energy Formulae
The work done or energy released is 1 joule when 1 coulomb moves between two points having a p.d. of 1 volt (p. 136). Hence, for $Q$ coulombs and $V$ volts,

$$\text{energy, } W = QV \text{ joules} = IVt \text{ joules} \qquad \ldots(1)$$

as $Q = I \times t$. Here $I$ is in amps, $V$ in volts, $t$ in seconds.

In the case of a resistance $R$, such as a lamp filament or electric heater, $V = IR$. (This relation for p.d. would not be true for the coil of an electric motor, for example, as the movement of the coil introduces another or induced p.d., p. 174.) Hence, from (1),

$$W = I^2 Rt \text{ joules} \qquad \ldots(2)$$

Also, using $I = V/R$,

$$W = \frac{V^2 t}{R} \text{ joules} \qquad \ldots(3)$$

### Power Formulae
Power, $P$ = energy per second = $W/t$,

$$\therefore P = IV = I^2 R = \frac{V^2}{R} \text{ watts}$$

since 1 watt is the rate of working at 1 joule per second (p. 25).
Units. Power: 1 kilowatt (kW) = 1000 watts (W). Energy: 1 kilowatt-hour (kWh) = energy used in 1 hour when the power is 1 kW. This is the Board of Trade unit in commercial electricity,

$\therefore$ number of kilowatt-hours

$$= \frac{\text{number of watts}}{1000} \times \text{number of hours used}$$

Example. A lamp is rated as '240 V–60 W'. (i) What does this mean? (ii) Calculate the resistance of the filament when the lamp is used. (iii) What is the cost of using 24 of these lamps and 12 240 V–100 W lamps continuously for 10 hours if the cost of a unit is 3p?

(i) This means that the power consumed by the lamp is 60 watts when the voltage applied is 240 volts.

(ii) From

$$P = \frac{V^2}{R}$$

$$\therefore 60 = \frac{240^2}{R}$$

$$\therefore R = \frac{240^2}{60} = 960 \text{ ohms}$$

(iii) Total power of lamps = $24 \times 60 + 12 \times 100 = 2640$ W,

$$\therefore \text{ energy used in kWh} = \frac{2640}{1000} \times 10 = 26\cdot4$$

$$\therefore \text{ cost} = 26\cdot4 \times 3\text{p} = 79\cdot2\text{p}.$$

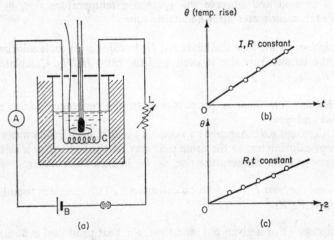

Fig. 133. Heating effect of current

*Heating Effect.*   Joule's laws state: The heat produced in a conductor is proportional to the square of the current, the resistance and the time.

*Verification.*   (1) Heat and time: *Method.* Use a heating coil C inside water in a calorimeter, with a suitable battery B, a rheostat L and an ammeter A (Fig. 133 (*a*)). Pass a constant current, stir the water and observe the temperature after every 30 sec.

*Calculation.*   Obtain the temperature rise $\theta$ from the instant of switching on and the corresponding times, *t*.

*Graph.*   Plot $\theta$ v. *t* (Fig. 133 (*b*)).

*Conclusion.* Since the graph is a straight line passing through the origin, the heat produced is directly proportional to the time, for a given current and resistance.

(2) *Heat and current: Method.* Using the same apparatus, pass known currents, such as 1·0, 1·5, 2·0, 2·5 amp, in turn through the coil for the same time, such as 5 min. Keep the current constant each time by means of the rheostat. Observe the temperature rise $\theta$.

*Graph.* Plot $\theta$ v. $I^2$ (square of the current) (Fig. 133 (*c*)).

*Conclusion.* Since the graph is a straight line passing through the origin, the heat produced is directly proportional to $I^2$, for the same time and resistance.

(3) *Heat and resistance:* (*a*) *Constant current.* Place two coils, resistances $R_1$, $R_2$, in *series*, each inside water in a different calorimeter. Pass a current and observe the respective temperature rise, $\theta_1$ and $\theta_2$, in each calorimeter after a suitable time.

*Calculation.* Calculate the heats $H_1$, $H_2$ in calories in each calorimeter from the temperature rise in each, and the ratio $H_1/H_2$. Calculate the ratio $R_1/R_2$.

*Conclusion.* The heat is proportional to the resistance for a given current and time.

(*b*) *Constant p.d.:* Arrange two coils *in parallel*, each inside water in a different calorimeter, so the same p.d. may be applied. After a suitable time, observe the temperature rise, $\theta_1$, $\theta_2$, in each calorimeter.

*Calculate* the heat $H_1$, $H_2$ in each calorimeter. This time it is found that $H_1/H_2 = R_2/R_1$.

*Conclusion.* For a given p.d. and time, the heat produced is *inversely-*proportional to the resistance.

*Formulae for Heat.* Joule's laws are contained in the electrical energy formula given on p. 146, namely,

$$\text{heat, } H = I^2Rt \text{ joules} = \frac{V^2t}{R} \text{ joules} = IVt \text{ joules} \qquad \ldots \text{(i)}$$

The unit of heat is now the joule (p. 22). Thus $H \propto I^2$ ($R$ and $t$ constant), $H \propto R$ ($I$ and $t$ constant), $H \propto t$ ($I$ and $R$ constant).

When two wires of 5 and 10 ohms are in *series* in a circuit, the same current passes through each. Hence, from $H = I^2Rt$, the heat in a given time in each wire is directly proportional to the resistance, or $H_1/H_2 = 5/10$. But if the same wires are in *parallel*, they have the same p.d. but a different current. Hence from heat, $H = V^2t/R$, the heat is *inversely*-proportional to the resistance, or $H_1/H_2 = R_2/R_1 = 10/5$. Thus, in contrast to the series case, a larger quantity of heat per second is liberated in the wire of *smaller* resistance. (Primarily, this is due to the larger current which flows in the smaller resistance.) A 240 V–100 W lamp has therefore a smaller filament resistance than a 240 V–60 W lamp, as lamps are connected in parallel with the mains voltage.

*Hot-wire Ammeter. Construction.* Consists of a thin resistance wire AB between two fixed points, with a taut phosphor-bronze wire CQ attached at C (Fig. 134). A silk thread attached at D passes round a grooved wheel W, the other end being attached to a spring S.

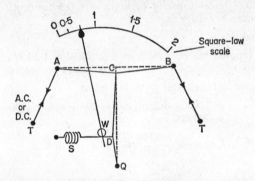

FIG. 134. Hot-wire ammeter

*Action.* When a current flows *via* terminals TT, AB becomes hot, expands, and sags at C. The sag is taken up by the spring, and a pointer P is deflected as the thread turns W.

*Scale.* Since the heat $\propto I^2$ for a given resistance, the scale is non-uniform or irregular (Fig. 134). The pointer deflects whichever direction the current flows, and hence the instrument can be used for both A.C. and D.C.

*Examples.* 1. Define *electromotive force*. Calculate the total energy provided by a battery of e.m.f. 2·50 volts when it causes a steady current of 0·40 amp to flow for 15 min through an electric bulb. If the battery had an internal resistance of 2·00 ohm, calculate the number of calories of heat dissipated in the electric bulb in that time. (L.)

Total energy provided = $EIt$ = 2·50 × 0·4 × (15 × 60) = 900 joules ...(1)

Heat dissipated in resistance = $I^2Rt$

$$= 0·4^2 \times 2^2 \times (15 \times 60) \text{ joules}$$

$$= 576 \text{ joules}$$

∴ heat dissipated in bulb = 900 − 576 = 324 J.

2. Calculate the resistance of the 1 kW heating element of an electric fire used normally on a 240-volt mains.

$$\text{Power spent} = \frac{V^2}{R} = \frac{240^2}{R} \text{ watts,}$$

where $R$ is the resistance of the element.

$$\therefore \frac{240^2}{R} = 1000$$

$$\therefore \quad R = 57 \cdot 6 \text{ ohm}$$

3. A kettle contains 2 litres of water and the electric power supplied is 2 kW. If the efficiency is 60%, find how long the water takes to reach boiling point from 20°C (Heat capacity of kettle = 400 J per degC, specific heat capacity of water = 4·2 J/g degC.)

Since efficiency is 60%,

$$\text{power reaching water} = \tfrac{3}{5} \times 2 \text{ kW} = 1 \cdot 2 \text{ kW}$$
$$= 1200 \text{ joules per second}$$

Energy needed to raise water to boiling point

$$= 2000 \times 4 \cdot 2 \times (100 - 20) + 400 \times (100 - 20)$$
$$= 704{,}000 \text{ joules}$$

$$\therefore \text{time} = \frac{704{,}000}{1200} = 587 \text{ s} = 9 \text{ m } 47 \text{ s}$$

# CHEMICAL EFFECT OF CURRENT OR ELECTROLYSIS

Dilute acid and salt solutions are liquids which conduct electricity well. Water is a poor conductor.

### Definitions

1. An *electrolyte* is a liquid which conducts electricity well.

2. The *anode* is the electrode dipping into the electrolyte connected to the positive side of the battery. The *cathode* is the electrode on the *negative* side of the battery.

3. A *voltameter* is a vessel containing the electrolyte and electrodes.

4. An *ion* is an atom or group of atoms carrying a negative or positive charge which is a simple multiple of the charge $e$ on the electron.

*Electrolysis of Copper Sulphate Solution.* (i) *Copper electrodes* (Fig. 135). At the cathode, copper is deposited; at the anode, an equal mass of copper is lost; the copper sulphate solution concentration remains constant.

Explanation: When the battery is connected, +ve ions drift through the electrolyte from the anode (+ve side of battery) to the cathode (−ve side). Thus +ve copper ions ($Cu^{2+}$) and +ve hydrogen ions

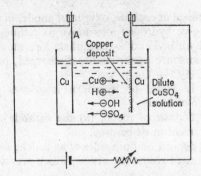

FIG. 135. Electrolysis of copper sulphate solution

(H⁺) reach the cathode—copper is preferentially discharged. The −ve ions, sulphate ($SO_4^{2-}$) and hydroxyl ($\overline{OH}$) drift in the opposite direction to the anode—copper ions from A go into solution.

(ii) *Platinum (or carbon) electrodes.* At the cathode, copper is deposited; at the anode, oxygen is given off; the concentration of copper sulphate solution alters.

Explanation: As before, copper ions are preferentially discharged at the cathode. At the anode, hydroxyl ions are preferentially discharged, producing oxygen—$4\overline{OH}^- \rightarrow 2H_2O + O_2 + 4e^-$.

*Electrolysis of Acidulated Water.* Electrolyte: water with a little sulphuric acid in a Hoffmann voltameter (Fig. 136). Anode and cathode: both platinum.

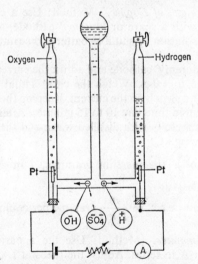

FIG. 136. Electrolysis of acidulated water

Hydrogen obtained at *cathode*, oxygen at anode, in volume ratio 2:1.

Explanation: +ve hydrogen ions move to cathode, where they are deposited. −ve hydroxyl and −ve sulphate ions move towards anode, where hydroxyl ions are preferentially discharged, producing oxygen. Thus: $4OH^- \rightarrow 2H_2O + O_2 + 4e^-$.

*General Rules.* 1. Metal or hydrogen is always produced at the *cathode* (−ve side of battery).

2. For a firm deposit of metal, (*a*) the cathode must be cleaned, (*b*) a moderate current must be used.

3. To obtain a deposit on both sides of an article, a circular anode or 'double' anode is used round the article, which acts as a cathode.

### Faraday's Laws

Law 1: The mass of an element deposited in a given voltmeter is proportional to the current and to the time.

Law 2: For a given current and time, the mass of an element deposited in electrolysis is proportional to its chemical epuivalent.

*Formula.* From Law 1,

$$m = zIt$$

where $m$ is the mass deposited by a current $I$ in a time $t$ and $z$ is a constant for the particular element called its *electrochemical equivalent.*

Definition: The 'electrochemical equivalent (e.c.e.)' is the mass of an element deposited by 1 ampere in 1 second or by 1 coulomb. Units: 'gramme per coulomb', g/C, or, in SI units, kg/C.

*Measurement of e.c.e. of Copper.* Method: Use a copper anode and copper cathode, with a spare or 'dummy' cathode, a beaker of dilute copper sulphate solution, a suitable battery, rheostat and ammeter in series.

First, use the 'dummy' cathode and adjust the current to be a suitable value, such as 0·5 to 1·0 A. Weigh the clean actual cathode C, place it in the beaker, and switch on the current. Keeping the current constant, pass it for a measured time, say 10 to 15 minutes. After switching off the current, wash C carefully with distilled water and then with ether, and allow to dry. Reweigh C.

*Calculation.* If $m$ is the mass in grammes, $I$ in amperes and $t$ in *seconds*, then

$$z = \text{e.c.e.} = \frac{m}{I \times t} \text{ gramme per coulomb}$$

*Calibration of Ammeter.* Method: Use the apparatus in Fig. 137, with the ammeter A in series. Adjust the rheostat L until the ammeter reading is 0·50 A. Carry out the experiment as above.

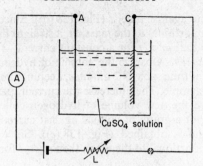

FIG. 137. Calibration of ammeter

*Calculation.* True current, $I = m/zt$; and knowing the e.c.e., $z$, of copper, $I$ can be calculated. Suppose this is 0·51 A. Then

correction to ammeter reading = $0·51 - 0·50 = 0·01$ A

The experiment is repeated for ammeter readings of 1·0, 1·5 A and so on.

*Verification of Faraday's First Law.* Method: Use a Hoffmann voltameter filled with acidulated water, connected to a suitable battery with an ammeter B and rheostat in series (Fig. 138 (a)).

1. *Mass and time.* Switch on the current, *keep it constant*, and observe the volume of hydrogen collected in equal intervals of time such as 30 sec.

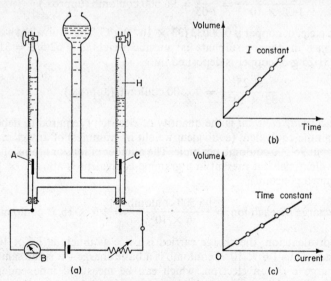

FIG. 138. Verification of Faraday's first law

Plot the volume against time, $t$ (Fig. 138 (*b*)). Since, approximately, the volume is proportional to the mass, $m$, a straight line graph through the origin shows that $m \propto t$ for a constant current.

2. *Mass and current.* Observe the volume of hydrogen collected in a suitable interval of time such as 2 minutes, keeping the current constant at 0·5 amp, for example. Then increase the current, pass it for the *same time*, and observe the new volume of hydrogen collected. Repeat for other currents. Plot a graph of volume against current. A straight line through the origin is obtained (Fig. 138 (*c*)). Since, approximately, the volume is proportional to the mass, then $m \propto I$ for a constant time.

*Verification of Faraday's second law.* Method: Place a Hoffmann volta-meter, filled with acidulated water (Fig. 136), in series with a copper volta-meter (Fig. 135), a rheostat, and a suitable battery. Switch on the current for a convenient time. Obtain the mass of copper deposited as described on p. 152 in the measurement of electrochemical equivalent, and the mass of hydrogen collected from the density of hydrogen, 0·09 g per litre at 0°C and 76 cm mercury pressure, after reducing the hydrogen volume to S.T.P.

Calculate the ratio of the masses. This will be found approximately 1:31·5, the ratio of the chemical equivalents of hydrogen and copper respectively.

*The Faraday: Charges on Ions.* The electrochemical equivalent (e.c.e.) of hydrogen is 0·0000105 ($1·05 \times 10^{-5}$)g/C. Thus 1 g of hydrogen, the equivalent weight, is deposited by

$$\frac{1}{1·05 \times 10^{-5}} = \frac{10^5}{1·05} = 96,500 \text{ coulomb (approx.)}$$

The e.c.e. of copper is 0·00033 ($33 \times 10^{-5}$) g/C. The equivalent weight of *copper* in copper sulphate is: atomic weight$/2 = 62·5/2 = 31·25$. Thus 31·25 g of copper is deposited by

$$\frac{31·25}{33 \times 10^{-5}} = 96,500 \text{ coulomb (approx.)}$$

The *faraday constant* is the quantity of electricity required to deposit the gramme-equivalent (equivalent weight in grammes) of any element. It is about 96 500 coulomb per mole. The number of ions or atoms of any monovalent element present in a gramme-equivalent is about $6 \times 10^{23}$ (Avogadro constant).

$$\therefore \text{ charge on each ion} = \frac{96\ 500 \text{ coulomb}}{6 \times 10^{23}} = 1·6 \times 10^{-19} \text{ coulomb}$$

On a divalent ion, the charge carried is twice as much as $1·6 \times 10^{-19}$ coulomb. Thus $1·6 \times 10^{-19}$ coulomb is a basic charge—it is the same as the charge $e$ on an electron, which can be measured independently (p. 195). Thus the charges carried by ions are multiples of the electronic charge, so that atoms become ions by losing or gaining one or more electrons.

*Examples.* **1.** What is the cost of depositing a layer of silver 0·2 mm thick on an object of total surface area 150 cm² if a current of 1 A used for an hour cost 2p.? (Density of silver is 10·5 g/cm³; electrochemical equivalent of silver is 0·00112 g/C.)

$$\text{Mass of silver deposited} = 150 \times 0·02 \text{ (cm}^3) \times 10·5 \text{ (g/cm}^3)$$
$$= 31·5 \text{ g}$$

$$\therefore \text{ number of coulombs required} = \frac{31·5}{0·00112} = 28,125$$

But cost of $1 \times 3600$ or 3600 coulomb is 2p.

$$\therefore \text{ cost} = \frac{28,125}{3600} \times 2p = 15·6 \text{ p.}$$

**2.** Given that the chemical equivalent of copper is 31·25 g and the faraday constant is 96 500 coulomb per mole, calculate (i) the current required to deposit 3·125 g copper in 10 hours, (ii) the quantity of electricity needed to deposit 5·4 g of silver if the chemical equivalent of silver is 108 g.

(i) Quantity of electricity in coulombs needed,

$$Q = \frac{3·125}{31·25} \times 96,500$$
$$= 9650$$

$$\therefore \text{ current, } I = \frac{Q}{t} = \frac{9650}{10 \times 3600} = 0·27 \text{ A (approx.)}$$

(ii) 108 g of silver is deposited by 96,500 coulomb,

$$\therefore 5·4 \text{ g of silver is deposited by } \frac{5·4}{108} \times 96,500 \text{ or } 4825 \text{ coulomb.}$$

# 8 Magnetism Electromagnetism Electromagnetic Induction

Strong magnets may be made from iron, nickel or cobalt alloys. They are called *ferromagnetic* materials. (Other elements are very weakly magnetic or non-ferromagnetic.) *Soft iron* is pure iron; the addition of a small percentage of carbon produces *steel*, a much harder substance. Temporary magnets (e.g. electromagnets) thus use soft iron; permanent magnets can be made with steel.

### Fundamental Rule
Like magnetic poles (N–N or S–S) repel: unlike poles (N–S) attract.
*Repulsion* between the pole of a compass A and one end of a steel bar B shows that the end of B is a pole or that B is a magnet. Attraction is never a sure test of magnetism because the compass pole would also be attracted if B were unmagnetized.

### Magnet, Non-magnet, Non-magnetic Material
Suppose three bars, A, B, C, of identical appearance are painted white. One is a magnet, another is not magnetized, and the third is non-magnetic, such as brass. To distinguish between them, suspend each in turn so they swing freely. The bar, B say, which always settles in a fixed direction approximately north–south, is the magnet.
Now bring B in turn to A and C. If C is attracted, this is the unmagnetized bar. A, which is unaffected by B, is non-magnetic.

### Making Magnets
1. *Strong magnet.* Place the steel bar inside a solenoid of many turns, connected to a suitable battery B (Fig. 139 (*a*)). Switch on a large

current for a short time and then switch off. Polarity: If the current at one end flows *clockwise* in the turns when viewed, this end is *south*, S. Anticlockwise = north, N.

2. *Weak magnet.* (i) Single touch: Stroke the steel bar repeatedly with the pole of a magnet—raise the magnet at the end of each stroke, otherwise the magnetism would be neutralized on returning (Fig. 139

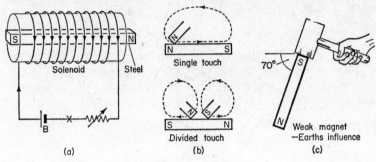

FIG. 139. Making magnets

(*b*)). Polarity: End last touched has *opposite* polarity to the stroking pole.

(ii) Divided (double) touch: Magnetize each half by repeated stroking with opposite poles (Fig. 139 (*b*)). Polarity: As for single touch.

*Note.* If like poles used, say two N-poles, the ends of the steel will both have S-poles and the middle will have a N-pole. The steel now has 'consequent poles'—it is not a magnet in the normal sense and it does not settle in any particular direction.

(iii) Hammering: Hold the steel bar at about 70° to the horizontal in a north–south direction. Hammer one end repeatedly. Polarity: In the northern hemisphere, the end pointing downward is N; in the southern hemisphere, that end is S. The earth's magnetic field induces the magnetism.

### Demagnetizing Magnet

Alternating current: Place the magnet inside a solenoid. Make sure the axis of the solenoid points east–west. Connect a low-voltage A.C. mains supply (Fig. 140). Now remove the magnet slowly from the solenoid to some distance away—it is practically demagnetized. Reason: The alternating current takes the material through 'cycles' of magnetization at the rate of 50 cycles per second. This makes the material magnetically softer and its magnetism soon disappears.

*Hammering* and *heating*, with the magnet pointing east–west, produces partial demagnetization.

## Domain Theory of Magnetism

Briefly, this states that tiny regions or *domains* in iron and steel or other ferromagnetic (crystalline) materials have resultant strong magnetism. The latter can be represented by a line with an arrow to show the direction of magnetism and labelled n–s (Fig. 141).

*Unmagnetized materials.* The magnetism in the domains acts in

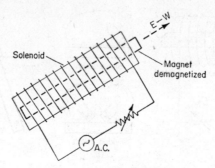

FIG. 140. Demagnetizing magnet

different directions and form 'closed chains' throughout the material (Fig. 141 (*a*)). There is no magnetism outside, as the poles neutralize each other.

*Magnets.* When the material is stroked repeatedly by a magnet the domains turn round under the magnetic influence and finally point one

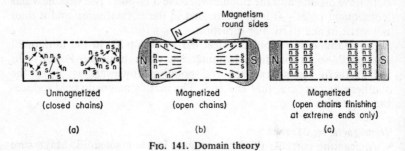

FIG. 141. Domain theory

way. Fig. 141 (*c*) is an ideal case—only the ends show 'free' poles, N and S. In practice, repulsion of similar poles at the ends also produces polarity round the *sides* of the magnet (Fig. 141 (*b*)).

*Experiments on Theory of Magnetism.*  1. Place some compass-needles near each other so that a 'closed chain' of magnets is formed. Bring near the pole of a magnet. The magnets now form 'open chains'.

Remove the magnetizing influence—the magnets from closed chains. Observe that a closed chain is a stable arrangement of magnets.

2. Fill a thin-walled test tube with iron filings. Place one end in turn near a suspended magnetic needle and observe the attraction each time. The iron filings are not magnetized. Now stroke the horizontal tube repeatedly with a powerful magnet as in magnetization by single touch. Bring the same end of the tube near the magnetic needle— repulsion occurs with one pole of the needle. The iron filings at this end are hence magnetized. Now shake the tube so the arrangement of filings is completely disturbed, and test the end once again. The magnetism disappears.

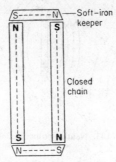

FIG. 142.  Keepers

*Keepers.* To prevent demagnetization, bar magnets are stored in pairs with *unlike* poles at each end and a *soft iron keeper* across the poles (Fig. 142). The keepers become magnetized and a *closed chain* of domains is obtained. This stable arrangement keeps the domains in the bar magnets in line, forming open chains here. Steel must not be used for a keeper—it would become permanently magnetized, and could be fitted wrongly, or disturb the magnetism, in the bar magnets.

### Magnetic Induction

Iron or steel become magnetized when near a magnet but not actually touching it. This is called magnetic *induction*. Mu-metal, very soft iron alloy, becomes magnetized in the earth's field when placed north–south.

Before attraction, a steel pin becomes magnetized by induction. *After* induction, it is attracted by the force between unlike poles.

## MAGNETIC FIELDS

A *magnetic field* is a region where a magnetic force can be detected. The *direction* of the field is chosen as the direction of movement of a *north* pole at the place concerned. Magnetic fields can be represented by drawing in them *lines of force*—a line of force is a line such that the tangent to it at any point represents the direction of the field there. The *density* of the lines (called 'flux-density') represents the strength of the field in the region concerned.

In drawing magnetic fields, (i) sketch a few typical lines rather than many lines, (ii) put arrows on the lines to show the field direction, always from north to south. Do *not* draw broken lines to represent lines of force, and remember that lines of force cannot cross.

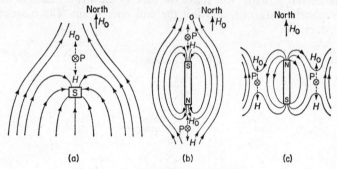

FIG. 143. Neutral points in fields

*Fields round Magnets.* (i) *Single pole* (Fig. 143 (*a*)). The earth's field, which is represented by straight parallel lines pointing northwards, combines with that of the single pole, represented by lines radiating outwards. No lines pass through P, called a neutral point. This is *a point where the resultant field is zero*. Here the earth's magnetic field, repre-

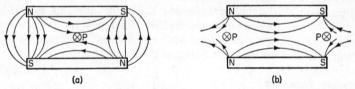

FIG. 144. Parallel bar-magnets

sented by $H_0$ in Fig. 143 (*a*), is exactly equal and opposite to the field due to the S-pole, represented by $H$.

(ii) *Bar magnet with S-pole pointing north.* Two neutral points, P, are obtained on the axis of the magnet (Fig. 143 (*b*)).

(iii) *Bar magnet with N-pole pointing north.* Two neutral points, P, are obtained, but east and west of the magnet (Fig. 143 (*c*)).

(iv) *Parallel bar magnets.* Neglecting the earth's magnetic field, a neutral point P is obtained with unlike poles facing (Fig. 144 (*a*)), and two neutral points, P, with like poles facing (Fig. 144 (*b*)).

*Iron in Magnetic Fields.* Soft iron concentrates the magnetic field where it is situated, creating a more powerful field, because it becomes powerfully magnetized. Fig. 145 (*a*) shows the concentrated field in a narrow gap between curved poles N, S of a magnet and a cylindrical soft iron core C, which occurs in the moving-coil instrument. Fig. 145 (*b*) shows the shielding effect of placing a soft-iron ring B round an instrument A in a magnetic field. Fig. 145 (*c*) shows the concentration of lines of force in a bar of very soft iron placed north–south in the earth's field. In each case the soft iron becomes magnetized. If the iron is

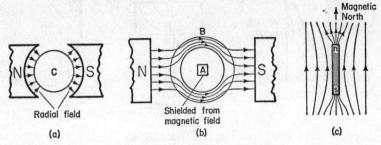

FIG. 145. Effects of soft iron in fields

removed, the lines pass from one pole to the other directly and the concentration of lines in the air, and hence the strength of the field, is now much less.

### Terrestrial Magnetism

The earth acts like a magnet. The north-geographical pole has *south* magnetic polarity since it attracts the north-pole of a magnet; the south-geographical pole has north magnetic polarity.

*Angle of Dip.* The *angle of dip* (*inclination*), δ, is the angle between the horizontal and the earth's total or resultant field, *R*. It is the angle between the horizontal and the direction of a freely-suspended needle N in the 'magnetic meridian', which is the vertical plane passing through the magnetic north–south direction (Fig. 146 (*a*)).

Measurement: Use a dip circle. (i) Turn the vertical circle A round until the magnetic needle M points vertically (Fig. 146 (*b*)). (ii) Note the position of A on a horizontal circle B graduated in degrees from the pointer C, which turns with A. (iii) Now turn A exactly 90° from this position (Fig. 146 (*c*). Then, since A is now in the north–south direction or magnetic meridian, the angle which M makes with the horizontal is the angle of dip.

*Angle of Declination* (*variation*). This is the angle between the magnetic meridian and the geographic meridian, *or* between the geographic (true) north–south direction and the magnetic north–south direction (Fig. 147 (a)).

Measurement: Use a magnetic compass and obtain the direction of the magnetic north–south. Now find the direction of the shortest shadow

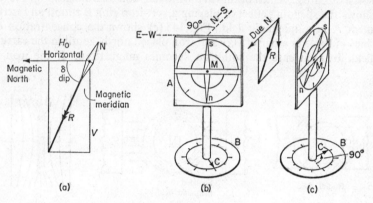

FIG. 146. Earth's field and dip

of a vertical pole at the same place—bisect the angle between the directions at 11 a.m. and 1 p.m. (Fig. 147 (b)). This gives the direction of the geographic north–south. The angle of declination can now be found.

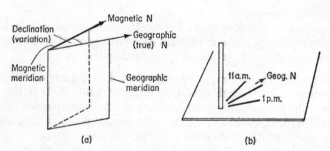

FIG. 147. Declination on variation

*Horizontal and Vertical Components.* Like any vector quantity, the total or resultant earth's magnetic field $R$ can be resolved into a *horizontal component*, $H_0$, and a *vertical component*, $V$. Fig. 146 (a) shows the parallelogram of forces for the earth's magnetic field. Since the angle of dip $\delta$ in Great Britain is about 65°, it follows that the vertical component $V$ here is greater than the horizontal component $H_0$.

## MAGNETIC EFFECT OF CURRENT

An electric current has a magnetic field round it. The appearance of the field depends on the shape of the conductor carrying the current, for example, straight wire or circular coil or solenoid.

*Demonstrations of Magnetic Effect.*    Straight wire: Hold an insulated straight wire *parallel* to a suspended magnetic needle NS and switch on

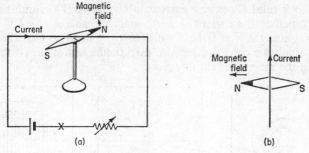

FIG. 148. Magnetic effect of current in straight wire

current (Fig. 148 (*a*)). Observe the deflection. The forces on N or S due to the magnetic field are always *perpendicular* to the current so they turn NS about its pivot. If the wire is held perpendicularly to NS and the current switched on, the needle does not move because the forces due to the magnetic field now have no turning effect about the pivot (Fig. 148 (*b*)).

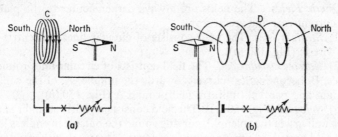

FIG. 149. Magnetic effect due to coils

Circular coil: Wind a wire into a *narrow coil* C and pass a current through it (Fig. 149 (*a*)). Hold near one face of the coil a suspended magnetic needle NS. Observe the attraction. Note the repulsion when the face of the coil is turned round.

Solenoid: Pull out the coil so that a *solenoid* D is formed (Fig. 149 (*b*)). As in the narrow coil, observe that each end of the solenoid has opposite magnetic polarity.

*Rules for Field Direction.* 1. Corkscrew rule: *Straight wire.* If the point of a corkscrew moves along the straight wire, the direction of rotation is the direction of the magnetic field round the wire. (Remember that 'direction of magnetic field' means the 'direction of movement of a *north* pole'.)

*Narrow Circular Coil and Solenoid.* If the corkscrew is rotated in the direction of the current, the direction of motion of the point is the direction of the magnetic field.

2. Clock rule: Clockwise current in circular coil = south magnetic pole. Anticlockwise current = north magnetic pole.

3. If a straight wire is held with the right hand so that the thumb points along the current direction, then the fingers of the clenched fist point in the magnetic field direction.

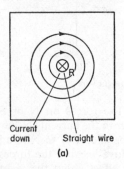
Current down    Straight wire
(a)

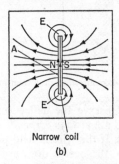
Narrow coil
(b)

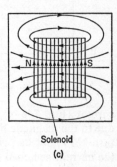
Solenoid
(c)

FIG. 150. Magnetic fields

*Magnetic Fields.* The fields are always perpendicular to the plane of the current-carrying conductor.

(1) *Straight wire.* The field consists of circular lines concentric with the wire R (Fig. 150 (*a*)).

(2) *Narrow circular coil.* The field consists of circular lines round the edges, E, becoming less curved towards the middle, A, of the coil, and straight and parallel (uniform field) round A (Fig. 150 (*b*)).

(3) *Solenoid* (Fig. 150 (*c*)). The field consists of fairly straight parallel lines well inside the solenoid, curving round the outside in endless loops. The field outside is similar to a bar magnet. Observe that the field inside the solenoid is practically constant or uniform along the length of it.

*Neutral Point with Straight Wire.* With the *earth's field* taken into account, a neutral point X is obtained on one side. The field direction due to the current, flowing downward at P in Fig. 151, is here shown by *H* acting due south. That due to the earth, shown by $H_0$, acts due north. The two fields neutralize each other. At a point, due west of the wire, the two fields assist each other as they act in the same direction. The lines of force are thus denser here than on the other side of the wire.

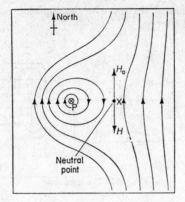

FIG. 151. Neutral point in combined field

*Battery Poles by Magnetic Effect.* To identify the unknown poles of a battery or other voltage supply, connect them to a circular coil or to a long straight wire. Observe the deflection of the north pole of a compass-needle brought near, as in Figs. 148 (*a*), 149 (*a*). Then, using Maxwell's corkscrew rule or clock rule, find the direction of the current in the conductor. This direction is *from the positive pole*, which is therefore identified.

*Electromagnets.* Coils are wound round *soft iron* cores. Observe that a clockwise current produces a *south* magnetic pole and that the coil windings are reversed on the two iron limbs to make one end a south and the other end a north pole.

*Electric Bell Circuit.* Has an electromagnet (soft iron), an armature (soft iron) with an attached springy metal resting lightly on a tungsten tipped (high melting point) screw. A circuit from a dry cell (used intermittently) is interrupted by make-and-break contacts, so that a clapper, attached to the armature, rings a gong repeatedly.

### Carbon Microphone

Contains carbon granules A, packed between two carbon blocks B, and a diaphragm C attached to one block (Fig. 152). A battery E passes steady current through the carbon granules before the person begins to speak.

Action: When a person speaks into the microphone, the varying sound pressure causes a corresponding variation of pressure on the granules. Closer together, their electrical resistance decreases. With looser contact, their electrical resistance increases. From Ohm's law, $I = E/R$, where $E$ is the battery e.m.f. and $R$ is the total resistance in the circuit. The (speech) current $I$ thus rises and falls at exactly the same frequency as the sound waves. The microphone has changed sound energy to electrical energy.

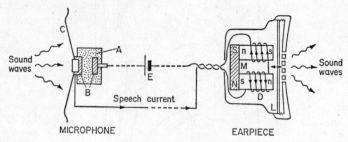

FIG. 152. The telephone

### Telephone Earpiece

This changes the electrical energy back to sound energy. It consists of coils, D ('speech coils'), wound round soft iron cores, with a permanent magnet M behind the latter and a thin soft iron diaphragm L in front (Fig. 152). The speech current from the microphone is passed into D.

Action: The speech current varies in magnitude. It therefore produces a corresponding variation in the strength of the magnetism in the cores. The attraction or pull on the diaphragm L thus varies at the same frequency as the speech current. L vibrates, and creates sound waves of the same frequency in the air, which is heard.

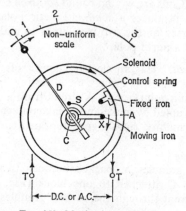

FIG. 153. Moving-iron ammeter

### Moving-iron Ammeter

The repulsion-type has a solenoid coil A, a fixed soft iron inside, a moveable soft iron X attached to a spindle C with an attached pointer D (Fig. 153). A spring S controls the movement of C. Fig. 153 shows a section of the coil and iron pieces.

Action: When a steady current flows in the solenoid through terminals T, the irons become magnetized. Since like poles face each other, repulsion occurs. When X moves, a deflection is obtained. If an *alternating current* is passed into A, the poles of the irons reverse continually. But like poles always face each other. Hence repulsion occurs and D is deflected again.

The scale is non-uniform because the repulsion depends on the strength of magnetization of the iron, which may vary non-linearly with the current. (A 'uniform' scale is obtained when the deflection is directly proportional to the current—see p. 174.) For an alternating current, the ammeter reading is the root-mean-square (r.m.s.) value of the current (p. 179).

## FORCE ON CONDUCTOR

A current in a wire produces a magnetic field round it. This may interact with another magnetic field in which the wire is situated. The wire moves from the strong to the weaker part of the combined field, that is, a *force* acts on it. Alternatively, since a current-carrying wire deflects a magnet (p. 163), by Newton's law of action and reaction in Mechanics, an opposite force, or reaction, acts *on the wire*.

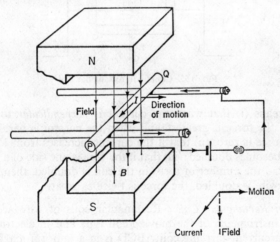

FIG. 154. Force on conductor

*Demonstration of Force.* A cylindrical metal bar PQ rolls along rails when a magnetic field B (north–south direction) is perpendicular to a current *I* in PQ (Fig. 154). Observe carefully (i) that the force reverses in direction when the field or current is reversed, (ii) that *no force acts when the field is parallel to the current*, (iii) that the magnitude of the force increases when the current *I* increases or the field strength increases or a longer conductor (more wire) is used in the same magnetic field.

The greatest force is obtained when the field is *perpendicular* to the current.

*Direction of Force.* Fleming's rule: If the first three fingers of the *left* hand are held mutually at right angles to each other, with the middle finger in the direction of the current and the fore-finger in the direction of the field, then the *thumb* points in the direction of *motion* or *force*.

*Magnitude of Force.* The force is directly proportional to the current *I*, to the strength of the magnetic field, to the length of wire concerned, and to sine $\theta$, where $\theta$ is the angle between the current and the field.

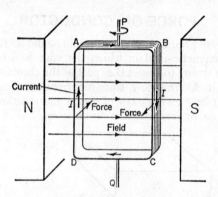

FIG. 155. Couple on rectangular coil

This means (i) that when the current is *perpendicular* to the field $(\theta = 90°)$ the force is greatest, and when the current is parallel to the field the force is zero, (ii) that if the current increases from 1 to 2 amp the force becomes doubled, (iii) that if the wire is one side of a rectangular coil, and the number of turns in the coil is doubled, then, since the length of wire is doubled, the force is twice as great.

*Couple on Rectangular Coil.* Rectangular coils of wire are used in electrical instruments of the moving-coil type and in electric motors. Suppose a current-carrying coil ABCD is in a uniform magnetic field (Fig. 155). The sides AD and BC are acted on by forces since they are perpendicular to the field; but the sides AB and DC have no forces on them, since they are parallel to the field. Observe that the force on AD is *opposite* in direction to the force on BC, which explains why the coil begins to *turn* about an axis PQ as shown. The two forces together are called a 'couple' in Mechanics.

After the coil turns, it settles down with ABCD facing the N- and

S-poles of the magnet. Forces still act on the sides AD and BC. But this time they act in the same straight line, and their resultant is hence zero.

*Clock rule.* The 'clock rule' can also be applied to find how a coil rotates in a magnetic field. From Fig. 155, the face ABCD acts like the S-pole of a magnet because the current flows clockwise. Hence this face is attracted to the N-pole of the magnet and repelled by the S-pole. Thus the coil rotates towards N.

### Moving-coil Instrument

This is the most accurate ammeter or voltmeter. It has (i) a rectangular coil *abcd*, (ii) a powerful permanent magnet with curved spherical poles N and S, (iii) a soft iron cylindrical core, (iv) an axle PQ in jewelled bearings about which the coil turns, (v) springs, oppositely wound, to control the coil rotation, (vi) a uniform (linear) scale (Fig. 156).

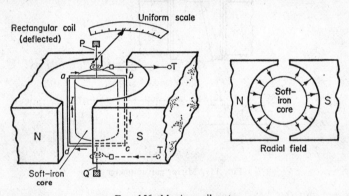

FIG. 156. Moving-coil meter

*Action.* The current-carrying sides *ad* and *bc* are perpendicular to the magnetic field between the core and the N- and S-poles—it is called a 'radial field' because the lines point along the radius towards the centre of the core. As on p. 168, the coil rotates. The turning-effect or moment depends on the magnitude of the forces $F$ on *ad* and *bc* and on their distance apart. In a radial field the distance apart is *always* the breadth of the coil. Hence the turning-effect or moment is proportional to $F$. But $F$ is proportional to the current $I$. *Thus the turning-effect proportional to $I$.* Hence the scale is a linear or uniform one.

Observe that (i) the *uniform (linear) scale* is due to the radial magnetic field—if the core were removed the scale would no longer be uniform, (ii) the *sensitivity*, that is, the deflection obtained per unit current, is greater if the springs are less powerful, or if the magnet is stronger, or if the coil has more turns.

*Mirror galvanometer.* This is the most sensitive form of moving-coil instrument (Fig. 157). (1) The springs are replaced by a long *phosphor-bronze torsion wire*, from which the coil is suspended—this has a very weak but definite control over the deflection, (2) the pointer is replaced by a concave *mirror* attached to the coil and a beam B of incident light, which is reflected along a scale D graduated in millimetres to give a measure of the current.

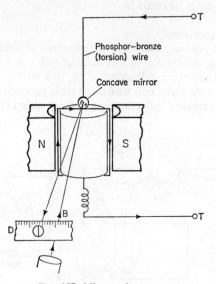

FIG. 157. Mirror galvanometer

*Milliammeter conversion to Ammeter.* To extend the range of a milliammeter, from 0–15 milliamp to 0–1·5 amp for example, *add a suitable resistor R in parallel* (Fig. 158 (*a*)).

Suppose the milliammeter coil has 5-ohms resistance. Then, with a current of 1·5 amp *outside*, a maximum current of 15 milliamp (0·015 amp) flows through the coil. Hence the current through $R = 1.5 - 0.015 = 1.485$ amp.

Now p.d. across $R$ = p.d. across 5-ohm coil = $0.015 \times 5 = 0.075$ volt,

$$\therefore R = \frac{V}{I} = \frac{0.075}{1.485} = \frac{5}{99} \text{ ohm}$$

*Milliammeter conversion to Voltmeter.* Suppose the 0–15 milliamp instrument needs to be converted to a 0–3 volt instrument. This time add a suitable resistor $S$ *in series* (Fig. 158 (*b*)).

A p.d. of 3 volts across both the 5-ohm coil and $S$ produces a full-scale deflection or a current of 15 milliamp. From Ohm's law,

$$\text{total resistance} = \frac{V}{I} = \frac{3 \text{ volt}}{0 \cdot 015 \text{ amp}} = 200 \text{ ohms}$$

$$\therefore S = 200 - 5 = 195 \text{ ohms}$$

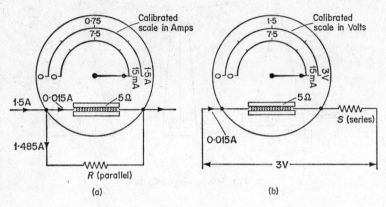

FIG. 158. Milliammeter to (a) Ammeter (b) Voltmeter

### Forces Between Currents

Currents in parallel wires, X and Y, in the *same* direction *attract* each other (Fig. 159 (*a*)). X is in the magnetic field due to Y. Fleming's

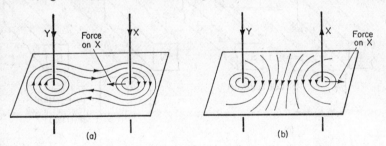

FIG. 159. Fields due to parallel currents

left-hand rule (p. 168) shows X is attracted to Y. Similarly, Y is attracted to X. Note the lines of force round both conductors.

If the currents are in the opposite direction, they *repel* (Fig. 159 (*b*)). To show which way X now moves, apply Fleming's left-hand rule. Note the repulsive effect of the lines of force.

*Ampere Balance.* The *ampere* is now defined in terms of the force between two current-carrying wires. It is the current in an infinitely-long conductor of negligible cross-section which repels a similar conductor one metre apart carrying an equal current in a vacuum with a force of $2 \times 10^{-7}$ newton (p. 16) per metre length of the conductors.

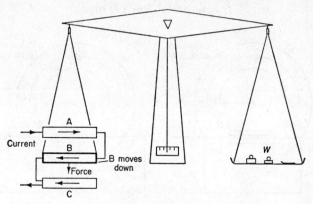

FIG. 160. Ampere balance

The principle of an ampere balance is illustrated in Fig. 160. Coils A and C are fixed; coil B is moveable and attached to one side of a sensitive balance. When a current flows through the three coils, B is repelled by A and attracted by C and hence moves downwards. The

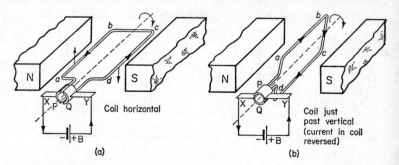

FIG. 161. Single motor

force is counterbalanced by weights *W*, and *W* is a measure of the magnitude of the current.

### Simple Electric Motor
This consists of a *coil of wire abcd* situated in the field due to a *magnet* N, S (Fig. 161). The terminals of the coil are permanently joined to the

two halves, P, Q, of a *split-ring commutator*, which turn round with the coil. Two *brushes* X, Y press against the commutator as it turns. A battery, B, is connected between X, Y.

Action: Suppose the current flows round the coil in the direction *dcba*. This face acts like a magnetic N-pole since it is anticlockwise. It is therefore attracted towards the S-pole of the magnet.

Just as the coil passes the *vertical*, the two halves of the commutator ring switch over brushes. Thus P, in contact with X in Fig. 161 (*a*), moves to make contact with Y in Fig. 161 (*b*). The current hence *reverses* in the coil. The coil face is now repelled by the S-pole, and therefore continues to turn instead of stopping. Remember that the

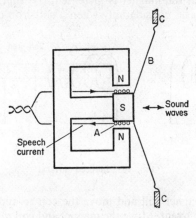

FIG. 162. Moving coil loudspeaker

current is automatically reversed by the commutator every time the plane of the coil passes the vertical.

The speed of rotation is increased (i) by using a larger current, or (ii) by increasing the strength of the magnetic field, or (iii) by using more turns of wire and bigger area of coil.

### Moving-coil Loudspeaker

A light coil (speech coil) A is wound round a former to which a large paper cone B is attached (Fig. 162). The coil is in the radial field of a permanent magnet N, S. A large (baffle) board C prevents sound waves from behind the cone flowing round to the front, which would produce a distorted sound.

Action: When a current flows in A, a force acts on it since it is in a radial magnetic field (compare *Moving-coil Instrument*, p. 169). The speech-current is a varying current. Hence the force varies. This makes the coil and attached cone B *vibrate* at the speech frequency. Thus sound waves of the same frequency are generated. A loud sound is produced because the area of the cone is large, thus disturbing a large mass of air.

# ELECTROMAGNETIC INDUCTION

### Basic Experiments

1. Move the N-pole of a magnet towards the face of a coil C joined to a galvanometer G, and then away from C (Fig. 163 (a)). Observe (i) that a current (induced) flows in C *only* while the magnet is moving, (ii) that the current reverses when the direction of movement of the magnet is reversed, (iii) that the magnitude of the current increases when the speed of the magnet is increased, (iv) that the magnitude of the current increases considerably when a soft-iron core is used inside the coil.

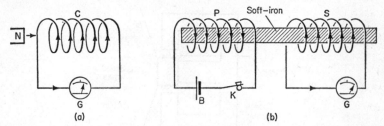

Fig. 163. Induced currents

2. Keep the magnet still and move the coil to-and-fro. Observe the varying induced current. Move the magnet and coil *together* at the same speed—observe there is no induced current.

3. *Primary and secondary coils.* Use a coil P, a 'primary' coil, with a key K and a battery B in place of a magnet (Fig. 163 (b)). Make and break the circuit and observe the opposite deflections in the neighbouring or 'secondary' coil, S. Repeat with soft iron in both coils and observe the much greater deflection.

### Laws of Induction

1. *Lenz's law* states: The induced current flows in such a direction as to *oppose* the motion or change producing it.

2. *Faraday's law* states: The induced e.m.f. is proportional to the *rate of change* of the lines of force linking the coil.

*Verification of Lenz's Law.* Push a N-pole towards a coil whose turns are visible, and observe which way the current flows through a connected galvanometer G. From the way the turns are wound, verify that the induced current flows *anticlockwise* when the N-pole is pushed forward. Thus the induced current flows so as to oppose the motion of the pole.

*Verification of Faraday's Law.* Rotate a coil at different constant speeds, and measure the steady induced current, $I$, each time on a sensitive galvanometer connected to the coil through a split-ring commutator. Measure the number of revolutions per minute, $n$, at each constant speed. A graph of $I$ v. $n$ is found to be a straight line passing through the origin, showing that $I \propto n$.

## Induction Coil

This changes a steady low voltage of say 6 to 12 volts to high voltage of several thousand volts in one direction. It has a primary coil P of a few hundred turns; a secondary coil S of several thousand turns; a

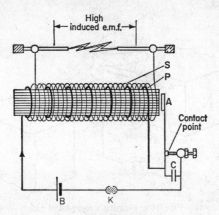

FIG. 164. Induction coil

soft-iron core in the form of insulated strips; a make-and-break device with a capacitor C across the contacts; and an accumulator B of 6 or 12 volts as the low-voltage supply (Fig. 164).

Action: When the circuit is made by K, the iron A is attracted to the core. This breaks the circuit and A then falls back again to the screw tip, so that the circuit is made and broken repeatedly.

The secondary coil has thus a change of lines of force through it. A high induced voltage is obtained at its terminals at the break because the current drops quickly to zero. A low induced voltage is produced at the make because the current takes a much longer time to reach its full value. An average high induced voltage is hence obtained at the secondary terminals. It is primarily due to the rapid change at the *break* of a large number of lines of force. Constructional features are: (1) a nickel-silver (high melting point) tipped screw, and a large capacitor across the contact points to absorb the energy which would otherwise produce excessive sparking; (2) the large number of turns in the secondary coil; (3) the soft-iron core.

*Induced e.m.f. in Straight Wire.*    An induced e.m.f. is obtained in a straight wire AB perpendicular to a magnetic field when it is moved at right angles to its length and to the field (Fig. 165). A movement in the reverse direction produces an opposite current in G.

Reason: The induced e.m.f. is due to the 'cutting' of lines of force when the wire is moved up or down. The faster the wire is moved, the greater is the induced e.m.f., since the rate of cutting is higher. Note that no induced e.m.f. is obtained when the wire moves *parallel* to the field since no lines are then cut.

Fleming's right-hand rule: Place the first three fingers of the *right* hand mutually at right angles, with the fore-finger in the direction of the

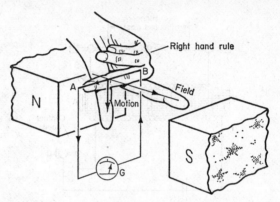

FIG. 165. Fleming's right-hand rule

magnetic field and the thumb in the direction of motion. Then the *middle* finger points in the direction of the induced e.m.f. In Fig. 165, A is the 'positive' or higher potential end, so that current flows outside in G from A to B.

*Earth's field.* A train moving east–west has wheel axles pointing north–south. The 'vertical component' of the earth's magnetic field (p. 162) produces a small induced e.m.f. along the axle, since movement, field and metal axle are mutually perpendicular. An induced current is also obtained in a coil rotated in the earth's magnetic field.

### Simple Dynamo
This produces an e.m.f. and current by rotation of a coil. (Do not confuse this with the 'electric motor', which is *supplied* with current from a battery.) The dynamo coil (or armature) rotates at constant speed in a fixed magnetic field (Fig. 166 (*a*)).

Action: Consider the coil *abcd* to be made of four pieces of straight wire. When the coil is *horizontal* at an instant, *ab* moves upward. The field, direction of movement and *ab* are all mutually perpendicular. Applying Fleming's right-hand rule, an induced e.m.f. is obtained along *ab*. Now (i) *cd* moves downward and hence an e.m.f. along *cd* is obtained, (ii) the sides *bc* and *ad* cut no lines as they rotate and hence no e.m.f. is obtained here.

Result: An induced e.m.f. and current is obtained in the coil in the direction *abcd*.

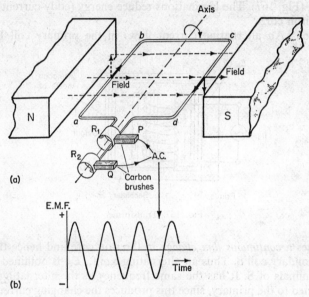

FIG. 166. Simple dynamo

Direction: The direction is constant while *ab* moves up and *cd* moves down. It *reverses* as the plane of the coil passes the vertical, because *ab* now moves down and *cd* moves up. Thus an *alternating* e.m.f. is obtained at the terminals. It changes in direction every time the plane of the coil passes the vertical or at every half-revolution. See Fig. 166 (*b*).

*Alternating current* (A.C.) is obtained by connecting the ends of the rotating coil to two rings $R_1$ and $R_2$, which turn with the coil. $R_1$ and $R_2$ press against fixed brushes P and Q, to which the outside circuit, such as a lamp, is connected for the current to flow. *Direct current* (D.C.) is obtained by using a split-ring commutator (see p. 173). The two halves change over brushes as the coil passes the vertical. Hence the current in the outside circuit, joined to the brushes, continues to flow in the same direction.

### Transformer

This changes alternating e.m.f. or voltage to a higher value (step-up transformer) or a lower value (step-down transformer). It does *not* work with steady or direct voltages.

Description: It has a *primary coil* P to which the voltage $E_P$ to be changed is connected; a *secondary coil* S from which the changed voltage $E_S$ is obtained; and a *soft-iron core* in the form of laminated (thin) sheets insulated from each other, round which both coils are wound (Fig. 167). The laminations reduce energy (eddy-current) losses in the iron core.

Action: An alternating current flows in the primary coil P. This

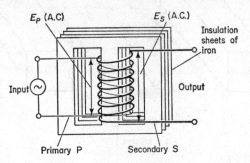

FIG. 167. Transformer

produces a *continuous flux change* in the iron core and hence through the secondary coil S. Thus an alternating e.m.f., $E_S$, is obtained across the terminals of S. It has the same frequency as the alternating e.m.f. connected to the primary, since this produces the changing current in P. The *magnitude of the e.m.f.* $E_S$ is proportional to the number of turns, $n_S$, in the secondary. Reason—the flux density is the same everywhere in the iron, and hence the total flux linking the coil at any instant is proportional to its number of turns.

Law: It follows that

$$\frac{E_S}{E_P} = \frac{n_S}{n_P},$$

where $n_P$ is the number of turns in the primary to which the e.m.f. $E_P$ is connected.

Suppose $E_P = 2$ volts A.C., $n_S : n_P = 60 : 1$ (step-up). Then

$$\frac{E_S}{E_P} = \frac{60}{1} \quad \text{or} \quad E_S = 60 \times 2 \text{ V} = 120 \text{ volts A.C.}$$

Suppose $E_P = 240$ volts A.C. and 12 volts A.C. is needed for operating a ray-box. Then a *step-down* transformer is needed. If

1000 turns are in the primary, the number required in the secondary is given by:

$$\frac{E_S}{E_P} = \frac{n_S}{n_P} \quad \text{or} \quad \frac{12}{240} = \frac{1000}{n_S}$$

$$\therefore n_S = 1000 \times \frac{1}{20} = 50 \text{ turns}$$

*Note.* Like any machine, the *power* obtained in the secondary is theoretically the same as that in the primary. Now power, $P = $ p.d. ($V$) × current ($I$). Thus a step-up in voltage, $V$, automatically results in a step-*down* in current, $I$. Thus a 240-volt mains transformer with a current of 2 A in the primary (= 240 × 2 = 480 watts) has a current in a 1200-volt secondary (step-up = 5) of 1/5 of 2 A or 0·4 A (= 1200 × 0·4 = 480 watts), assuming no power losses. In practice, the power in the secondary is less than that in the primary owing to losses.

*Demountable Transformers.* These can demonstrate (i) induced (eddy) currents in metals—water inside a metal ring placed round the core can be made to boil, (ii) the high current in the secondary of a step-down transformer—a fuse wire connected to the secondary terminals burns out, (iii) the induced e.m.f. in the secondary—a bulb connected to a coil of wire lights up when the coil is placed over the iron core.

## *A.C. Principles*

1. The *peak value* or amplitude of an alternating current or voltage is the maximum value during a cycle.

2. A.C. produces no chemical effect since the current reverses continuously, and no deflection in the moving-coil instrument because the coil and needle are unable to follow the frequent reversals. It produces *heat* in a wire since this is independent of direction (heat $\propto I^2$).

3. The *root-mean-square* (*r.m.s.*) value of an alternating current or voltage is the square root of the average of the *squares* of all the values of current or voltage over a cycle. Alternatively, the r.m.s. value is the *steady* value of current or voltage which produces the same heating effect per second in a wire as the alternating current or voltage. For a sine-wave A.C., r.m.s. = 0·7 × peak value (approx.).

*A.C. Measurement.* Use (i) a moving-iron repulsion instrument (p. 166) or (ii) a hot-wire ammeter (p. 149) for measuring the r.m.s. value. A cathode-ray oscillograph (p. 194) measures the peak value—the height of the wave-trace on the screen represents twice the peak value and this can be found by comparing it with the trace due to a known voltage.

*Resistors, capacitors, coils.* *Resistors* R allow both A.C. and D.C. to flow (Fig. 168 (*a*)).

*Capacitors* (*condensers*) C do not allow D.C. to flow—they have an insulating medium (dielectric) between their plates (p. 186). By using a small lamp in series with a large capacitor, one can see that A.C. flows in the circuit (Fig. 168 (*b*)). The varying voltage charges the capacitor

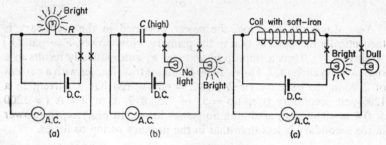

FIG. 168. A.C. and D.C. effects

continuously and the corresponding varying movement of charges occurs in the wire so that A.C. flows.

Coils of wire allow both A.C. and D.C. to flow. The coil opposes the varying flux which passes through it, from Lenz's law (p. 174). A soft-iron core increases the flux linking the coil and hence also the 'opposition' to flow of A.C. If a ray-box is connected in series with a coil and a 12-volt A.C. supply the lamp burns brightly. But the light becomes dimmed when a bar of soft iron is pushed into the coil, owing to the much greater opposition to current flow (Fig. 168 (*c*)).

# 9 Electrostatics

Electric charges appear on insulators when they are rubbed. They do not stay on rubbed metals held in the hand—metals and the human body are *conductors* and the charge quickly leaks away. The electric charges are due to millions of electrons transferred by rubbing *either* from the insulator to the rubbing material *or* from the rubbing material to the insulator. The charge on an insulator is static.

## Positive and Negative Charges

Definitions: A *positive charge* is that on a glass rod rubbed with silk. A *negative charge* is the charge on an ebonite rod rubbed with fur.

An electron was found to have a negative charge (p. 191). A rubbed polythene rod has a negative charge; a rubbed cellulose acetate or perspex rod has a positive charge.

*Law:* Like charges (two positive or two negative) repel. Unlike charges (positive and negative) attract.

## Gold-leaf Electroscope

This has a metal terminal or *cap* A connected to a *gold leaf* or leaves L at the bottom B of a metal rod (Fig. 169). The leaf is surrounded by a metal case C, with plane glass windows, and C is usually earthed to 'screen' the leaf from stray charges.

*Testing Charges.* By touching the cap with a charged rod, give the leaf a negative charge. Now bring up an *unknown* charge X slowly to the cap A (Fig. 169). If the leaf diverges more, then X is a negative charge. If the leaf divergence diminishes on bringing an object Y near A, then Y *may* have a positive charge or it may be uncharged. The only sure test of charge is an increased divergence. So re-charge the leaf *positively* and bring Y again near A. If the leaf opens wider, then Y has a positive charge. If the divergence diminishes again, it was uncharged.

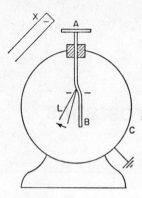

FIG. 169. Testing charge by electroscope

### Static and Current Electricity

1. Connect a high p.d. between the cap and case of an electroscope (e.g. a few thousand volts from a safe E.H.T. source). After switching on, disconnect the cap lead by an insulating rod R so that the leaf stays open.

Test the charge by bringing a positive or negative charge near the cap. The leaf has a +ve charge when the +ve terminal is connected to the cap, and a −ve charge when the −ve terminal is connected.

Repeat with the 240-volt A.C. mains, connecting the insulated line (live) lead to the cap. This time note that the leaf sometimes has a +ve charge and sometimes a −ve charge, depending on the particular half of a cycle at the moment of disconnection.

Conclusion: The electricity from the E.H.T. or mains supply is the same kind as that on charged rods.

2. Charge a large insulated metal sphere by a Van de Graaff machine or other method. Connect one terminal of an insulated sensitive moving-coil mirror galvanometer to earth and touch the other with the sphere. The small deflection shows that a magnetic effect is produced when static charges move (p. 170). Static electricity is the same kind as that obtained from cells.

### Testing Conducting Powers and Quantities of Charge

1. *Conducting powers* of particular pieces of silk, cotton and metals are roughly compared by connecting them in turn between the cap and case of a charged electroscope, and observing the time taken for the leaf divergence to fall by half. The faster the fall, the greater is the conducting power.

2. *Quantities of charge* on insulated metal spheres X and Y are roughly compared by placing a deep metal can A on the cap of an

electroscope, and lowering X until it touches the bottom. This is repeated with Y. The divergence of the leaf in each case is proportional to the quantities of electricity on X and Y (see *Faraday's Ice-pail Experiment*, p. 184).

### Induced Charges

An *induced charge* is one acquired by an object without any contact with the charge used. (Compare 'Magnetic induction', p. 159.)

Method: Suppose an insulated metal sphere Y needs to be charged by induction. (*a*) Bring a −ve charge rod X near Y, but *not* touching, (*b*) earth Y by touching it with the finger, (*c*) remove the finger, (*d*)

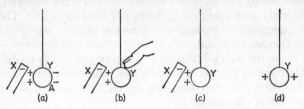

FIG. 170. Induction

finally remove X (Fig. 170). Note that the rod X must be kept in position near Y after the finger is removed, and is taken away *last of all*. The induced charge on Y is always *opposite* to the inducing charge.

Explanation: (i) On bringing the −ve charge near to Y, the electrons

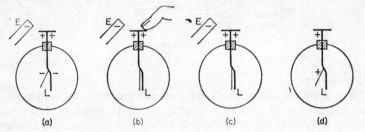

FIG. 171. Charging electroscope by induction

(−ve charges) in the metal are repelled to A. (ii) When Y is touched, the electrons now escape through the body to earth. (iii) Y has therefore now a *positive* charge. (iv) When X is removed the positive charge spreads symmetrically over Y. Note that if X is removed after Y is touched as in Fig. 170 (*b*), then the electrons return from earth and Y has no charge.

*Charging Electroscope by Induction.* The stages are illustrated in Fig. 171. This time the movement of electrons away from the end L through the body is shown by the leaf closing (Fig. 171 (*b*)). After the rod E is removed, the positive charge spreads to the leaf, which then opens.

*Faraday's Ice-pail Experiment.* This provides information about induced charges and shows how a charge can be completely transferred.

Experiment: Lower an insulated charged metal sphere S into a deep metal insulated can connected to a gold leaf electroscope (the leaf opens), touch the bottom and observe the leaf (the divergence remains constant), and then remove S and test its charge (no charge remains on S).

Deductions: (i) The induced negative charge on the inside of the can has completely neutralized the inducing positive charge on S. Thus when a metal *completely* surrounds an inducing charge, the induced and inducing charges are equal.

(ii) The charge on a metal such as S can be *completely* transferred to an electroscope by placing it inside a deep conductor connected to the cap (see p. 181); whereas touching the electroscope cap directly only transfers part of the charge.

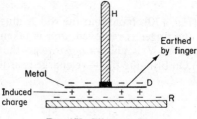

FIG. 172. Electrophorus

### Electrophorus

This is a simple arrangement for producing charges by induction. It has a metal disc D with an insulating handle H, which is placed on a rubbed perspex or other insulator R which may be negatively charged, say (Fig. 172). D has very few parts actually in contact with R—an air-film is between D and R. Thus on touching D momentarily with a finger the induced negative charge passes to earth, leaving D with an induced *positive* charge. After removal from R a spark passes from D to a knuckle or other earthed object, so that D has an amount of energy. It is derived from the work done in removing the positive charge on D from the attracting negative charge.

### Van der Graaff Machine

In a simple form, a silk or polythene belt B moves round two insulated rollers X and Y (Fig. 173). Suppose the belt acquires a negative charge by friction with Y. The charge is carried upwards to a pointed conductor P connected to the large smooth hemisphere S, and a positive charge is induced on P and a negative charge on S. By the action of points, positive charge from P 'sprays' the belt in front, thus discharging it.

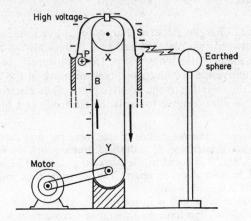

FIG. 173. Van der Graaff generator principle

When the belt moves down to Y and round again, the action is repeated. The induced charge on S grows and the voltage rises to several thousand volts or more because S is a large smooth hemisphere. The energy in a spark obtained from S comes from the work done in moving the negative charge on B towards the top against a repulsive force—this energy is supplied by the motor.

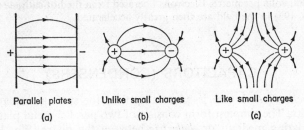

Parallel plates          Unlike small charges      Like small charges

(a)                          (b)                          (c)

FIG. 174. Electric fields

## Electric Fields

An electric field is a region where an electric force is experienced. Electric fields are produced round isolated charges, or between conductors such as metal plates connected to the terminals of a battery.

Some electric *lines of force* are shown in Fig. 174. Note that the arrows on the lines show the movement of a *positive* charge in the field (compare *magnetic lines of force*, p. 160). To demonstrate electric lines of force, use metal plates dipping into a light oil which has semolina or grass seed sprinkled on its surface. When an E.H.T. battery is connected to the metals, the fine particles arrange themselves along the lines of force.

*Movement of Charges.* Positive charges (e.g. +ve ions in an electrolyte) situated between two plates joined to a battery always move from the positive to the negative plate. See p. 150. Conversely, negative charges, such as negative ions or electrons, tend to move in the opposite direction, from the negative to the positive plate. Thus electrons liberated in a radio valve always move towards the electrode at a higher potential.

*Force on charge.* The magnitude of the 'force per unit charge' in a field is called the 'electric intensity', $E$, of the field. Numerically, the intensity between the plates A and B is equal to the *potential gradient*, $V/d$, where $V$ is then p.d. and $d$ is their distance apart. The intensity thus increases when $V$ increases and $d$ is made smaller.

When $V$ is in volts and $d$ in metres (SI system), then intensity, $V/d$, is in 'volts per metre'. The force on a charge of 1 coulomb in a field intensity of gradient 1 volt per metre is 1 newton (p. 16). Hence the force on an electron of charge $1 \cdot 6 \times 10^{-19}$ coulomb between two plates having a potential gradient of 200,000 volts per metre $= 1 \cdot 6 \times 10^{-19} \times 200,000 = 3 \cdot 2 \times 10^{-14}$ newtons. This is a tiny force, but the mass of an electron is only about $9 \times 10^{-31}$ kgm. Hence from $F = ma$, the acceleration $a = F/m = 3 \cdot 2 \times 10^{-14}/ 9 \times 10^{-31}$ metre per $\sec^2 = 3 \times 10^{16}$ metres per $\sec^2$ (approx.), which is an enormous acceleration.

In radio valves a p.d. of a few hundred volts may be set up across metals only a few millimetres apart, thus creating a potential gradient of the order of 100,000 volts per metre. Electrons liberated from the hot cathode C of the valve (p. 193) in the field are then greatly accelerated.

# CAPACITORS (CONDENSERS)

A *capacitor (condenser)* is an arrangement for storing a quantity of electricity. The simplest form consists of two parallel metal plates with an insulating medium or *dielectric* between the plates (Fig. 175 (*a*)). Air, paper and mica are examples of dielectrics.

### Charging a Capacitor
Connect a battery to the plates (Fig. 175 (*a*)). Electrons flow for a short time from A to B. In a 'model' capacitor such as two large parallel plates A and B, A can be charged by contact with a rubbed polythene or other rod. The charges, $Q$, in each plate are equal and opposite.

## Discharging Capacitor

Connect the two plates A and B together by a piece of wire (Fig. 175 (ii)). Electrons return from B to A and neutralize the positive charge completely. Both plates then have no charges.

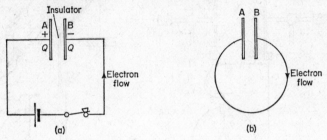

FIG. 175. Charging and discharging capacitor

## Capacitance

Definition: Capacitance, $C = Q/V$, where $Q$ is the charge on either capacitor plate when $V$ is the p.d. applied to the plates.

When $Q$ is 1 coulomb and $V$ is 1 volt, the capacitance is 1 *farad* (F). The *microfarad* ($\mu$F) is the capacitance when 1 microcoulomb of electricity is obtained by the capacitor when a p.d. of 1 volt is applied. Thus 1 $\mu$F = one-millionth F.

## Factors Influencing Capacitance

The capacitance $C$ depends on (i) the *common area A* between the plates, (ii) their distance $d$ apart, (iii) the nature of the dielectric or medium between the plates.

*To investigate the effect of d.* Connect two parallel metal plates A, B to the cap and case of a gold-leaf electroscope (Fig. 176 (*a*)). Remember that the divergence of the leaf is always a measure of the *potential difference*, $V$, between the cap and case. Charge A by contact with a rubbed polythene or other rod. Now move B (earthed) nearer A. The divergence diminishes. Thus $V$ decreases. Since the charge $Q$ keeps constant, then, from $C = Q/V$, $C$ increases.

*Effect of Common Area.*   Use a metal foil F on an *insulated* roller in place of the plate A (Fig. 176 (*b*)). As the foil is rolled up after charging it, thus diminishing the common area with B, the leaf divergence increases. Hence $V$ increases. Thus, from $C = Q/V$, $C$ decreases.

*Effect of Dielectric.*   Keeping the two metal plates A, B in Fig. 176 (*a*) fixed, place glass, paper or other dielectrics between them. The leaf divergence diminishes. Hence, from $C = Q/V$, $C$ increases.

Summarizing: $C$ increases when the common area $A$ increases, the

distance apart $d$ decreases, and dielectrics such as paper replace the air
between the plates.

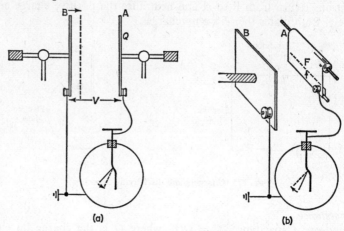

FIG. 176. Variation of capacitance

*Types of Capacitors*
1. *Variable air (tuning) capacitor.* This has two sets of plates, F and M,
each insulated from the other. One set M can be rotated, so that the
common (overlapping) area varies (Fig. 177 (*a*)).

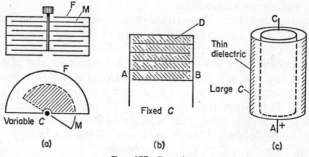

FIG. 177. Capacitors

2. *Multiplate condenser.* This has two sets of metal plates, A and B,
with an insulator such as mica, D, between them (Fig. 177 (*b*)).
3. *Electrolytic capacitor.* This has a very thin dielectric of aluminium
oxide formed on the anode A of two aluminium 'plates' in a suitable
electrolyte. Since $d$ is so small, a very large capacitance, such as 200 $\mu$F,
can be obtained in a small volume (Fig. 177 (*c*)). A must always be at a
higher potential than the cathode C when the capacitor is used in a
circuit.

# 10  Electron Physics

### Cold and Hot Cathodes

*Cold Cathode.* Cathode rays, or electrons, are produced in low-pressure air (0·01 mm mercury) inside a long glass tube when a high p.d. (e.g. 5000 V) is connected across metal electrodes A and C at either end. Electrons move at high speed from the cold cathode C (−) to the anode A (+) (Fig. 178). They produce a glow on a fluorescent screen beyond A.

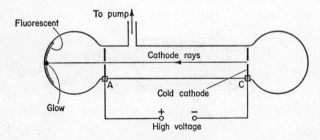

FIG. 178. Discharge Tube

*Hot Cathode.* Electrons are emitted by connecting a low voltage (4, 6 or 6·3 V D.C. or A.C.) to a fine tungsten wire, which becomes hot. Some of the free electrons inside the metal gain sufficient energy to escape and exist outside the metal. This is similar to boiling water, when molecules escape and form a vapour outside the surface, and is called 'thermionic emission'. The oxides of barium and strontium emit electrons at a much lower temperature than tungsten wire.

### Electron Demonstration Tubes

1. TELTRON *tube.* This has a hot cathode C inside a vacuum. A cylindrical anode A has a p.d. of several thousand volts relative to C. High-speed

electrons then pass through A and produce fluorescence on striking a coated screen at O (Fig. 179).

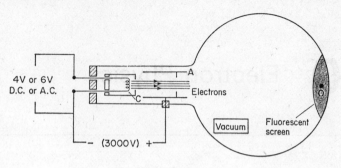

FIG. 179. Electron tube

2. LEYBOLD *fine-beam tube*. This has a hot cathode C inside a tube containing low-pressure hydrogen. A cone-shaped anode A, with a hole at the top, has a positive potential of a few hundred volts relative to C. A fine luminous beam PQ is produced when the electrons collide with molecules of the gas (Fig. 180).

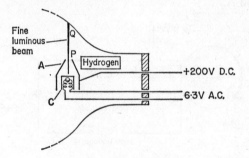

FIG. 180. Fine beam tube

### Electron Energy

The energy of the electrons colliding with the screen in the vacuum tube, or with the gas molecules in the fine-beam tube, comes from the energy of the battery or voltage supply between the anode and cathode.

The quantity of electricity, $e$, on an electron is $1 \cdot 6 \times 10^{-19}$ coulomb (approx.). Suppose the p.d. between anode and cathode is 300 volts. Then, since the energy gained by 1 coulomb in moving through 1 volt is 1 joule (p. 136),

$$\text{energy gained per electron} = 1 \cdot 6 \times 10^{-19} \text{ (coulomb)} \times 300 \text{ (volts)}$$
$$= 4 \cdot 8 \times 10^{-17} \text{ joule}$$

One million ($10^6$) electrons moving from cathode to anode would hence gain $10^6 \times 4\cdot8 \times 10^{-17}$ or $4\cdot8 \times 10^{-11}$ joule.

The *colour* of the beam in the fine beam tube depends on the nature of the gas used, such as hydrogen. The colour of the light on the screen in the vacuum tube depends on the nature of the fluorescent material. The *intensity* of the light depends on the number of electrons per second passing the anode.

### Electron Properties

1. They travel in straight lines—a sharp shadow of a metal Maltese cross inside the tube is obtained on the glass.

2. They have momentum—a paddle wheel turns when exposed to electrons.

3. They have energy—metals exposed to electrons become hot.

4. They produce fluorescence in certain materials.

5. They are extremely light—they are easily deflected by a powerful (e.g. Ticonal) magnet. The mass of an electron = 1/2000th mass of hydrogen atom (approx.).

6. They carry a negative charge (see later).

*Sign of Charge on Electron.* Use a Perrin tube, which has a Faraday cylinder M inside it, a hot cathode C and an anode A, all in a vacuum (Fig. 181). Join M to the cap P of a leaf electroscope and the case Q to

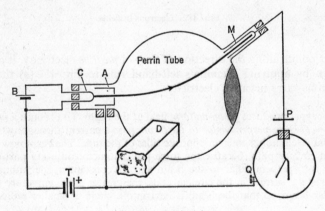

FIG. 181. Perrin tube

A. Switch on the voltage supplies (B is a few volts, T is an E.H.T. supply of a few thousand volts). Now bring up a powerful magnet D perpendicular to the beam and move it until the electron beam is deflected into M, as in Fig. 181.

The leaf now diverges. Using an insulated rod, disconnect the lead from P. Bring up a negatively-charged rod. The leaf opens wider, showing the charge is negative.

### Electrons in Magnetic and Electric Fields

*Magnetic Field.*    Bring up the S-pole of a powerful magnet perpendicular to the luminous beam in a fine beam tube. The beam is deflected and curves in an arc (Fig. 182 (i)). Compare the deflection of a current-carrying wire in a magnetic field, p. 167. Remembering that the middle

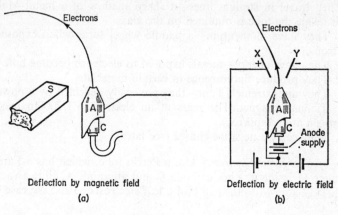

Deflection by magnetic field
(a)

Deflection by electric field
(b)

Fig. 182. Electrons in fields

finger points along the direction of flow of *positive* electricity, it can be shown by applying Fleming's left-hand rule to Fig. 182 (*a*) that the electrons carry negative electricity.

A magnet produces a *non-uniform* field at the beam. To produce a *uniform field everywhere perpendicular to the beam,* pass a current through two large circular (Helmholtz) coils on opposite sides of the tube. The beam now bends into a *circular* path, because the force per centimetre on every part of the beam is (i) perpendicular to the beam and (ii) constant in magnitude. The stronger the current in the circular coils, the greater is the curvature of the circular beam, so that the beam is bent into a circle of smaller radius.

*Electric Field.*    Obtain an electric field between the two plates X and Y of a fine beam tube by joining a battery of a few hundred volts to the plates (Fig. 182 (*b*)). Connect the anode A to the centre of the battery. When X is made +ve relative to Y, the beam is deflected in an arc towards X, as shown; when X is made −ve relative to Y, the beam is deflected towards Y.

### Diode Valve

This is a two-electrode valve (Fig. 183 (a)). It has a glass envelope, completely evacuated, containing (1) a hot cathode, C, which emits electrons, (2) a metal anode, A. This collects electrons when a battery, B, is connected so that A is +ve in potential relative to C, but *not* when −ve relative to C. Thus:

*a diode allows current through it only when A is positive relative to C*

*Characteristic ($I_a$–$V_a$) Graph.* This is POLMN—note the zero current part, PO, of the characteristic (Fig. 183 (b)).

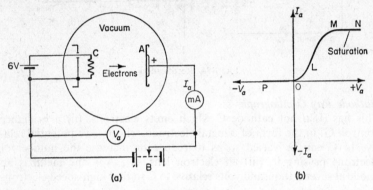

FIG. 183. Diode valve

Explanation: Electrons moving from C to A create a 'space-charge', which is negative. At low positive voltages of $V_a$, anode voltage, it repels many electrons back to C so that the anode current $I_a$ is low. At higher voltages of $V_a$ the attraction round C is stronger; and so more electrons reach A and $I_a$ increases.

When $V_a$ reaches a particular high +ve voltage, *all* the electrons emitted by C reach A—any further increase in voltage hence produces no increase in current, which is called the *saturation current*. The latter can only be increased by raising the cathode temperature, for example, by increasing the current in it.

*A.C. to D.C. Voltage. Rectification. Diode rectifier.* To obtain D.C. from A.C. voltage, connect a diode D in series with a resistor R to the A.C. voltage V (Fig. 184 (a)). A voltage in one direction, $V_0$, though not steady, is obtained across R.

Explanation: On one half of the A.C. cycle, say HK, the anode A is +ve relative to C. The diode hence conducts and a voltage is obtained across R (Fig. 184 (b)). On the other half KL of the same cycle, A becomes −ve relative to C. The diode does not conduct. This is repeated. The voltage across R has thus an average D.C. value as shown.

A *metal rectifier* consists of a series arrangement of copper discs oxidized on one side—this conducts well in the cuprous oxide-copper direction but very poorly in the opposite direction. Unlike the diode valve it allows a small current to flow on the negative half of the a.c. cycle, but the voltage across $R$ is again an average d.c. value.

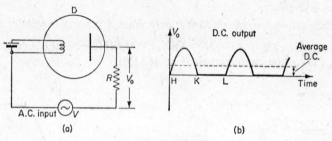

FIG. 184. Rectification

### Cathode Ray Oscillograph

This has (i) a hot cathode C which emits electrons, (ii) a brilliance control, G, in the form of a metal electrode, whose −ve potential relative to C can be varied so as to reduce or increase the number of electrons passing it, (iii) an electron lens, $A_1$, $A_2$—one metal is an anode at several thousand volts relative to C so that high-speed electrons

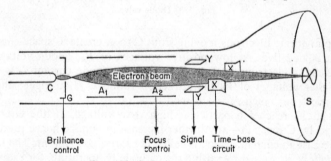

FIG. 185. Cathode ray oscillograph

are obtained and the other has a similar potential which can be varied to focus the electron beam on the screen, (iv) the screen S is painted with zinc sulphide or other fluorescent material which glows when struck by high-energy electrons. S is connected to the anode by painting the inside of the tube with conducting paint, thus ensuring that the electrons lose no energy after passing through the electron lens.

*Signal plates.* Any radio signal or voltage to be detected is connected between the Y-plates—this makes the beam move up and down.

*Time-base.* To show a signal's wave-form, the beam is also swept horizontally to-and-fro by a varying voltage joined to the X-plates from a 'time-base' circuit. When the time-base frequency is altered and is an exact number of times the signal frequency, a whole number of stationary waves is seen on the screen.

### Charge on Electron

In electrolysis the current through the solution is carried by *ions* (p. 150). Ions carry charges numerically equal to $e$ or $2e$ or $3e$, depending on their nature. Experiment shows 96 500 coulombs (faraday constant) is required to liberate the gram-equivalent (equivalent weight in grams) of any element. Now about $6 \times 10^{23}$ (Avogadro constant) atoms are present in the molecular weight of a monatomic element such as silver, which is also its equivalent weight. Hence, from electrolysis,

$$\text{charge carried by each ion} = \frac{96,500 \text{ coulomb}}{6 \times 10^{23}}$$
$$= 1\cdot6 \times 10^{-19} \text{ coulomb (approx.)}$$

Direct measurement of the charge on an electron by Millikan confirmed this value for $e$.

### Millikan Experiment

*Method.* 1. Connect two parallel plates A, B to a variable high-voltage d.c. source $V$ (Fig. 186). 2. Squeeze the oil spray until a drop of appreciable size is seen in the microscope M. 3. Then hold the drop *stationary*

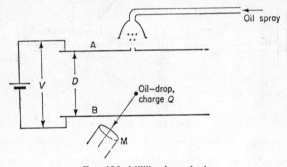

Fig. 186. Millikan's method

by applying a suitable opposing field, viewing it for a long time. Note the voltage $V$ now applied. 4. Switch off the supply voltage and allow the drop to fall. Observe the time taken to fall between the two fixed hair-lines in the miscroscope, a known distance $s$ apart. If more readings are required the drop can be brought up again by reversing the field. 5. Repeat for several drops. 6. Note the air temperature and pressure.

*Theory.* Suppose the charge on the drop is $Q$, the mass of the drop is $m$, its radius is $a$, the density of oil is $d$, the viscosity of air is $\eta$, and the time is $t$ for the drop to fall the distance $s$. Then, for equilibrium of drop, neglecting the small upthrust in air, and noting $V/D$ is the electric intensity,

$$mg \text{ (weight)} = \frac{VQ}{D} \text{ (upward force due to electric field)} \qquad \ldots\text{(i)}$$

When drop falls freely in air with its terminal velocity,

$$mg = 6\pi\eta a \times \text{velocity} = 6\pi\eta as/t \qquad \ldots\text{(ii)}$$

$$\therefore \frac{4}{3}\pi a^3 dg = 6\pi\eta a \frac{s}{t},$$

since $m$ = volume of drop × density. Solving for $a$, the mass $m$ of the drop can then be calculated. From (i), the charge $Q$ can be found. This will be a multiple of $e$, the charge on an electron. The smallest charge of all the many values for $Q$ is a measure of $e$.

# X-RAYS

*Nature.* X-rays are electromagnetic waves of very short wavelength of the order of $10^{-8}$ cm. Thus they have the same nature as light waves (electromagnetic waves) but about 1000 times shorter in wavelength.

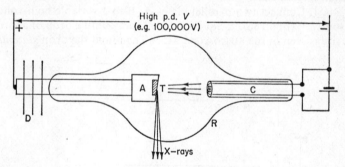

FIG. 187. X-ray tube

*Production.* X-rays are produced when high-energy electrons collide with metal atoms and penetrate close to the nucleus. Then:

*energy of incident electrons (100%)*
*= energy in X-ray beam (0·1%)*
*+ energy as heat in metal (99·9%)*

*X-ray Tube.* This has (1) metal target T, (2) copper anode A, (3) hot cathode C, (4) cooling arrangement such as fins D for anode, (5) tube R containing a vacuum (Fig. 187).

C has a low-voltage supply (e.g. 4 V) connected to it. A very high p.d. $V$ (e.g. 100,000 V) is connected between A and C. The energy and hence the penetrating power of the X-rays increases when $V$ increases.

*Properties.* 1. X-rays penetrate tissue or flesh and are dangerous to health. They are partially stopped by bone and materials of high density, and are therefore used in radiography.

2. X-rays are diffracted by crystals, whose atoms are closely spaced at intervals of about $10^{-8}$ cm and act like a diffraction grating (p. 94). Diffraction photographs hence yield information on the atomic structure of crystals in metals or other materials, a subject called 'X-ray diffraction analysis'.

# 11 Radioactivity Atomic Structure

## Radioactive Sources

A radioactive source is one which emits ionizing particles or radiation due to the instability of the nuclei of its atoms.

The radioactivity is unaffected by changes in temperature or pressure or by chemical combination of the atoms concerned. These changes are unable to affect the nucleus of an atom.

Generally, radioactive sources emit $\alpha$-, $\beta$-particles or $\gamma$-rays, or a mixture of them. Weak sources are used in school laboratories. They must always be handled with tongs and replaced in their lead containers immediately after use.

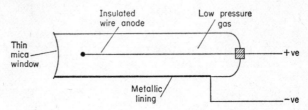

FIG. 188. Geiger-Müller tube

## Radioactive Detectors

1. *Geiger-Müller (GM) Tube.* Detects $\alpha$-, $\beta$-particles and $\gamma$-rays. Contains a small amount of gas with an insulated wire inside kept at a high potential, for example, four or five hundred volts relative to the casing in one form of tube (Fig. 188).

An $\alpha$- or $\beta$-particle or $\gamma$-ray has sufficient energy to ionize the gas, that is, some electrons are torn off atoms of the gas, leaving them as positive ions. The high voltage on the wire then produces many more electrons and ions—the electrons are accelerated to high speeds and collide with other atoms. The sudden burst of current results in a momentary or 'pulse voltage' in a resistor (not shown) in the positive lead. Each ionizing particle or radiation produces a pulse voltage.

A *scaler* is a device which has electronic counting tubes and an electromagnetic counter. If a GM tube is connected to a scaler, each pulse voltage is automatically recorded. Thus the scaler measures the actual number of ionizing particles or radiations in a given time. The *count rate*, the number per second or minute, is a measure of the *intensity* of the radiation.

A *ratemeter* measures the intensity directly when a GM tube is connected to it. A microammeter records an average current which is proportional to the intensity.

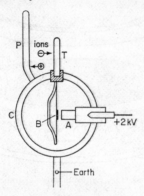

FIG. 189. Pulse electroscope

2. *Pulse (Wulf) Electroscope.* This detects only α-particles. It is a sensitive electroscope with a side electrode A at a high potential (Fig. 189). A metal 'flag' B on a fibre under tension is connected to a terminal T insulated from the case C, which is earthed. Initially, T is at the same potential as A.

When the air in the neighbourhood of T is exposed to α-particles, it becomes ionized. The drift of ions between T and P lowers the potential of T and produces a pulse or 'beat' of the flag. The rate of the pulses or beats is a measure of the intensity of the α-particles or radioactivity of the source.

3. *Solid State Detector.* This detects α-particles readily, and can also detect β-particles and γ-rays. It has a semiconductor device which produces a burst of current on exposure to ionizing particles, and this can be detected on a scaler or ratemeter connected in the circuit.

4. *Spark Counter.* This detects only α-particles. A fine wire X, is kept at a high potential a small distance above an earthed metal base.

α-particles ionize the air between X and the base, and sparks are produced here.

5. *Diffusion Cloud Chamber.* A little methyl alcohol is poured on to the felt ring R, fixed against the top of the perspex cover D, so that it is soaked in alcohol (Fig. 190). The velvet base B is also dampened with alcohol and the perspex top is replaced. A small amount of dry ice is placed in the lagged compartment L underneath the chamber so that it is in contact with the brass plate P, and the base is replaced.

Place the cloud chamber upright on a level surface and illuminate it

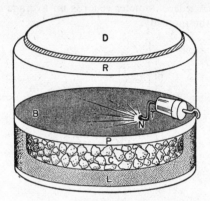

FIG. 190. Diffusion cloud chamber

from the side with a strong light. Rub the perspex top with a duster to charge it and to attract all the dust particles in the air inside the chamber. Streaks or tracks can be seen on viewing from above when an α-particle source of radiation is on the point of a needle N inside the chamber.

*Explanation.* Alcohol evaporates from the felt ring which is at room temperature. The vapour diffuses or sinks to the lower part of the chamber, which is cooled to an extremely low temperature by the dry ice. In the absence of dust particles the vapour becomes supersaturated. Droplets then form round the ions produced by the passage of radioactive particles, so that their tracks are seen.

6. *Wilson Cloud Chamber.* The top is removed from this chamber, the black absorbent pad at the bottom is soaked with alcohol, and the top is then replaced. A radioactive source is placed in the chamber, which is illuminated from the side. A hand vacuum pump is connected to the base of the chamber by means of a valve. Dust particles are cleared as described before, or by applying an electric field with the aid of a high-tension battery. After the pump is operated, streaks or trails, formed by the passage of α-particles, are seen.

*Explanation.*   When the pump is operated, the alcohol vapour in the chamber becomes supersaturated owing to its expansion and consequent cooling. Droplets now form on the ions produced by the passage of radioactive particles, thus rendering the tracks visible.

*Detection of Alpha-, Beta-particles and Gamma-rays.*   A GM tube can be used with a scaler or ratemeter to distinguish between α- and β-particles and γ-rays. Remember that:

1. A thin paper stops α-particles but allows β-particles and γ-rays through.

2. An aluminium plate a few millimetres thick stops β-particles but allows γ-rays through.

3. A very thick lead block, of the order of a metre, will stop γ-rays. An absorption experiment can thus distinguish between the three types of radiations.

4. If a γ-source is moved twice as far from the GM window, the count rate diminishes to about one-quarter of its orginal value—*radiation intensity obeys an inverse-square law* (compare light intensity).

## Properties of Alpha-, Beta-particles and Gamma-rays

1. *Nature.*   (i) α-particles are relatively heavy particles carrying a positive charge $+2e$, where $e$ is the numerical value of the charge on an electron—they are *nuclei of helium*, that is, atoms of helium which have been stripped of two electrons.

(ii) β-particles are electrons—they are very light, have a mass about one–two thousandth of the mass of a hydrogen atom, and carry a negative charge $-e$.

(iii) γ-rays are not particles. They are electromagnetic waves (like light) with extremely short wavelengths less than $10^{-8}$ cm.

2. *Effect of Magnetic Field.*   In a powerful magnetic field at right angles to their direction, α-particles are deflected slightly (they are heavy), β-particles are deflected considerably in the opposite direction (they are light), (iii) γ-rays are unaffected (they are waves).

3. *Penetrating Power.*   (i) α-particles are easily absorbed by thin foil or paper. (ii) β-particles have higher penetration but are stopped by aluminium plate a few millimetres thick. (iii) γ-rays have very high penetrating power—they are stopped only by very thick lead blocks or concrete.

4. *Ionizing Power.* (i) α-particles produce considerable ionization in air —as their energy is used up quickly their range in air at normal pressures is very low. (ii) β-particles produce much smaller ionization in air—they have a longer range than α-particles since their energy is used up much less quickly. (iii) γ-rays produce a very small amount of

ionization in air—consequently they have a greater range than $\beta$-particles which have the same initial energy.

Using their ionization property, the GM tube is designed to detect $\alpha$- or $\beta$-particles or $\gamma$-rays but cannot distinguish between them directly; the pulse electroscope detects $\alpha$-particles only; the spark counter detects $\alpha$-particles only; and the diffusion cloud chamber detects $\alpha$-particles and only very energetic $\beta$-particles.

In contrast, the solid state detector uses a solid and not a gas and $\alpha$-particles produce ionization of the solid.

### Half-life
Definition: The time taken for half the atoms initially present to decay. The half-life varies with different radioactive substances but is a constant for a particular substance.

Measurement: Using a GM tube and scaler, determine the count

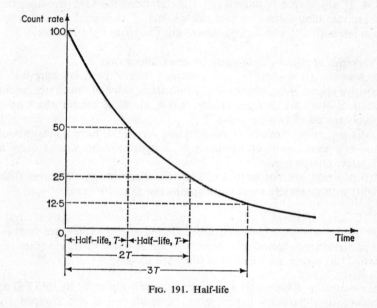

FIG. 191. Half-life

at the end of suitable equal consecutive periods of time, and hence the average count rate. Plot a graph of count rate v. time, and from it determine the time T for the count rate to diminish to half its initial value (Fig. 191).

Note that, for a radioactive substance with a very long half-life, the number of emissions in consecutive equal short periods of time fluctuates randomly, showing that the disintegration of atoms is a random process.

*Examples.* 1. The count rate from a scaler when a radioactive substance X is investigated is initially 300 per minute. If the rate drops to 75 per minute in 4 min, what is the half-life?

If the half-life is $x$ min, then the count rate decreases to $\frac{1}{2} \times 300$ or 150 per min in $x$ min. In another $x$ min the count decreases to $\frac{1}{2} \times 150$ or 75 per min. Thus

$$2x = 4 \quad \text{or} \quad x = 2$$

so that the half-life is 2 min.

2. The half-life of a radioactive substance is 1 min. If a reading of 200 microamp is obtained on a ratemeter at a given time, what is the reading 3 min later?

1 min later, the reading falls to $\frac{1}{2} \times 200$ or 100 microamp

Thus

3 min later, the reading falls to $\frac{1}{2} \times \frac{1}{2} \times \frac{1}{2} \times 200$ or 25 microamp

# ATOMIC STRUCTURE. NUCLEAR ENERGY

## Particles in Atoms

*Electrons* are particles carrying a negative charge, $-e$, which have a mass about one two-thousandth of the mass of a hydrogen atom. Electrons are outside the central core or nucleus of the atom. Symbol: $\bar{e}$ or $_{-1}^{0}e$.

*Protons.* A proton is the nucleus of a hydrogen atom. It therefore carries a positive charge, $+e$. It is practically as heavy as the hydrogen atom since the electron is so light. Protons are in the *nuclei* of atoms. Symbol: $_{1}^{1}H$.

*Neutrons.* A neutron is a particle in the nucleus which is practically as heavy as the proton but carries no charge. Symbol: $_{0}^{1}n$.

## Atoms

1. *Hydrogen atom.* Has a proton as the nucleus and one electron moving round it (Fig. 192 (i)).

2. *Other atoms.* Have (i) a nucleus containing neutrons and protons, (ii) a number of electrons, equal to the number of protons, moving round the nucleus (Fig. 192). Since the mass of the electrons is so small, the mass of the atom is practically concentrated in its nucleus. The positive charge on the nucleus is numerically equal to the total negative charge on all the electrons round it.

The diameter of an atom is of the order of $10^{-8}$ cm. The diameter of a nucleus is over ten thousand times smaller. The space inside the atom round the nucleus is thus largely empty.

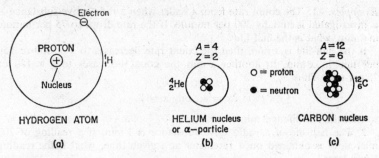

FIG. 192. Atoms and Nucleus

### Atomic Number. Mass Number

*Atomic number.* 1. The number of protons in its nucleus is called the *atomic number*, $Z$, of the atom concerned. It is equal to the number of electrons round the nucleus of the normal atom. There are 29 protons and 29 electrons in a copper atom; the atomic number is 29. The nuclear charge is $+29e$.

Note that the chemical behaviour of an element depends on its atomic number, $Z$, and *not* its atomic weight, since the shell structure of the orbiting electrons governs the chemical behaviour.

2. The *mass number*, $A$, of an atom is the total number of protons and neutrons in its nucleus. A copper nucleus has 29 protons and 34 neutrons so that the mass number is 63.

Note that the chemical *atomic weight* is an average value for the mass per atom of the element. Since elements contain atoms of differing mass (see *Isotopes* below), the atomic weight is rarely a whole number.

*Examples of mass number and atomic number.* An atom is represented by writing the mass number at the top of the chemical symbol and the atomic number at the bottom.

$^1_1\text{H}$ represents a proton—the hydrogen nucleus has a mass number 1 and carries a charge $+1e$ (Fig. 192 (*a*)). (i) The neutron, $^1_0\text{n}$, has a mass about the same as a proton and carries no charge.

$^4_2\text{H}$ represents a helium nucleus or $\alpha$-particle—it has 2 protons and 2 neutrons, and carries a charge $+2e$ (Fig. 192 (*b*)).

$^{235}_{92}\text{U}$ represents a uranium nucleus—it has 92 protons and 143 neutrons, and carries a charge $+92e$.

$^0_{-1}\text{e}$ represents a $\beta$-particle in the form of an electron—it has negligible mass and a charge $-e$.

*Isotopes.* 'Isotopes' are atoms with the same number of protons but a different number of neutrons. Thus their atomic number is the same but their mass number is different. $^{35}_{17}\text{Cl}$ and $^{37}_{17}\text{Cl}$ are isotopes of chlorine. Each has 17 protons and thus 17 electrons, so their chemical nature is the same. But one has 18 neutrons and the other 20 neutrons, so the mass of the latter nucleus is more than the former. Ordinary chlorine has 4 times as many atoms of mass number 35 as atoms of mass number 37. Hence

$$\text{atomic weight} = \frac{(4 \times 35) + (1 \times 37)}{5} = 35 \cdot 4$$

*Radioactive isotopes* are unstable isotopes which emit α- or β-particles and γ-radiation.

### Nuclear Changes

1. *Emission of α-particle.* An α-particle is a helium nucleus; it is represented by $^4_2\text{He}$ since it has a mass number 4 and an atomic number 2 or charge $+2e$. If a uranium nucleus $^{238}_{92}\text{U}$ emits an α-particle, the nucleus which remains changes in mass number and atomic number (Fig. 193 (*a*)). Thus a new element, thorium (Th), is formed:

$$^{238}_{92}\text{U} \rightarrow {}^4_2\text{He} + {}^{234}_{90}\text{Th}$$

Note that the total mass number and the total atomic number on the right side is equal to the original mass number and atomic number of uranium. The atomic number 90 is that of the element thorium, Th.

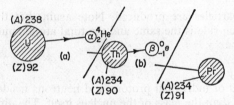

FIG. 193. Effect of emission

2. *Emission of β-particle.* A β-particle which is an electron has negligible mass and a charge $-e$. If it is emitted by a nucleus the mass number thus remains unaltered; but the atomic number *increases* by 1 (Fig. 193 (*b*)). A new element is hence formed. Since the β-particle has a very small mass, the new element has practically the same mass as the original element and they are called *isobars* (compare *isotopes*, p. 204). Thus suppose a β-particle is emitted from a thorium nucleus, $^{234}_{90}\text{Th}$:

$$^{234}_{90}\text{Th} \rightarrow {}^{\;0}_{-1}\text{e} \; (\text{β-particle}) + {}^{234}_{91}\text{Pr}$$

The new element, protactinium, and thorium are isobars.

*Example.* A uranium nucleus of mass number 238 and atomic number 92 emits in succession a total of 2 α-particles and 3 β-particles (electrons). What is the mass and atomic number of the nucleus remaining?

1. *Mass number.* An α-particle has a mass 4, a β-particle has negligible mass.

∴ mass number of remaining nucleus $= 238 - 2 \times 4 = 230$

2. *Atomic number.* An α-particle has a charge $+2e$, a β-particle (electron) has a charge $-1e$.

∴ atomic number of remaining nucleus $= 92 - 2 \times 2 + 1 \times 3 = 91$

### Nuclear Reactions

When a tiny particle such as an α-particle penetrates into the nucleus of an atom, and another particle such as a proton is ejected, (i) the total mass number on one side of the nuclear reaction = the total mass number on the other side, (ii) the total atomic number on one side = the total atomic number on the other side. Thus suppose an α-particle is incident on a nitrogen nucleus, $^{14}_{7}N$, and a proton, $^{1}_{1}H$, is ejected. Then:

$$^{4}_{2}He + {}^{14}_{7}N \rightarrow {}^{1}_{1}H + {}^{17}_{8}O$$

*The nucleus left is that of an oxygen atom, since the atomic number is 8.*

Suppose protons bombard on lithium nucleus, $^{7}_{3}Li$, and two identical particles are obtained from the nuclear reaction. Then:

$$^{7}_{3}Li + {}^{1}_{1}H \rightarrow {}^{4}_{2}He + {}^{4}_{2}He$$

Thus two α-particles are produced. Note again that the total mass number on each side is the same and the total atomic number on each side is the same.

### Nuclear Energy

The total mass of individual protons and neutrons inside a nucleus is always greater than the mass of the nucleus itself. The difference in the masses is a measure of the energy stored in the nucleus. If a nucleus is disrupted and the *mass change* is $m$, then, from Einstein's *mass-energy relation*, the energy $E$ released is given by

$$E = mc^2$$

$E$ is in joules if $m$ is in kg and $c$ has the value $3 \times 10^8$.

### Nuclear Fission

This is the name given to the 'splitting' of the uranium nucleus into *two* heavy parts when a neutron penetrates into it.

Example:

$$^{235}_{92}U + {}^{1}_{0}n \rightarrow {}^{148}_{57}La + {}^{85}_{35}Br + 3{}^{1}_{0}n \qquad \ldots(1)$$

A large amount of energy per gramme of uranium is released; this is proportional to the difference in masses of the total mass on each side of equation (1).

Since three neutrons are produced when one uranium atom undergoes fission, each neutron may then produce fission of three more uranium atoms, thus yielding nine neutrons, and so on. Hence the number of atoms undergoing fission may multiply rapidly—this is called a *chain reaction*—and a large amount of energy as heat may then be produced in a short time.

*Atom Reactor Principle.*    Basically, a reactor contains uranium-235 rods inside graphite blocks, which moderate the speed of the neutrons. They are then able to produce fission of uranium nuclei and produce a chain reaction. Gas circulating through holes in the graphite is heated by the energy released, and this is transferred to an external 'heat exchanger' in which water circulates. Steam is then produced and is used in steam turbines for generating electricity.

### Nuclear Fusion

In contrast to nuclear fission, where heavy elements break up, very light elements release energy when their nuclei fuse together to form heavier elements.  This is called *nuclear fusion*. Isotopes of hydrogen may fuse together to form helium if the hydrogen gas is heated to many millions of degrees C. This is called a *thermonuclear reaction* and takes place in the heart of the sun, thus releasing a stream of energy.

# 12 Gravitation Planetary Motion

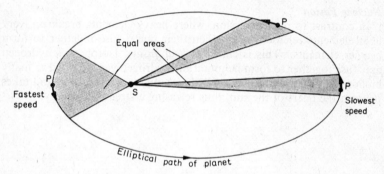

FIG. 194. Kepler's second law—equal areas swept out in equal times

**Kepler's laws.** These were deduced by Kepler from astronomical observations by Tycho Brahe:

1. Planets move round the sun in ellipses, with the sun at one focus of the ellipse. Fig. 194.

2. The line joining the sun and a planet sweeps out equal areas in equal times. See Fig. 194.

3. The ratio $T^2/R^3$ is a constant for each planet, where $R$ is the average radius of the orbit and $T$ is the period or time for 1 revolution. See Fig. 195.

**Newton's Law of Gravitation.** This states that the force of attraction $F$ between two masses $M_1$, $M_2$ whose centres are distance $R$ apart is given by

$$F = G\frac{M_1 M_2}{R^2},$$

where $G$ is a universal constant called the *gravitational constant*. See Fig. 195.

*Explanation of Kepler's third law.* A planet is kept in a circular orbit of radius $r$ by a centripetal force equal to $mv^2/r$, where $m$ is its mass and $v$ its speed. Hence from Newton's law, for planets moving round the sun of mass $M_s$, we have

$$\frac{mv^2}{r} = \frac{GM_s m}{r^2}$$

Thus $v^2 = GM_s/r$. Now the period $T = 2\pi r/v$, so $T^2 = 4\pi^2 r^2/v^2$. Substituting for $v^2$,

$$\therefore T^2 = \frac{4\pi^2 r^3}{GM_s}$$

Since $G$ and $M_s$ are constant, $T^2/r^3 = $ constant.

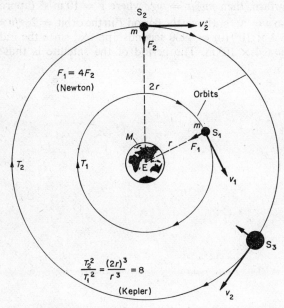

FIG. 195. Earth (E) satellites—illustrating Newton's law and Kepler's law

*Mass of sun.* Knowing $T$, $r$ and $G$ for a planet such as the earth, $M_s$ can be found from the equation above for $T^2$.

*Mass of earth.* Knowing $T$, $r$ and $G$ for the motion of the moon round the earth, the mass of the earth can be calculated from a similar equation.

**Notes.** (1) The *speed* (a 'scalar') of an object in a circular orbit is constant; the velocity (a 'vector') of the object changes continuously in the orbit because its direction changes. See Fig. 195.

(2) In an elliptical orbit, a planet moves *faster* near the sun to sweep out equal areas in equal times, Kepler's second law. See Fig. 194.

(3) The distance of the moon from the earth is about 60 times the radius of the earth. Since the gravitational attraction outside the earth $\propto 1/r^2$, where $r$ is the distance from the centre, the value of $g$ at the earth's surface becomes 'diluted' to a value $g/60^2$ at the moon.

(4) On the moon's surface, objects fall with an acceleration of about $g/6$, $\left(\dfrac{g(\text{earth})}{g(\text{moon})} = \dfrac{80}{3\cdot6^2} = 6 \text{ (approx.)},\right.$ since mass of earth $= 80 \times$ mass of

moon and radius of earth $= 3\cdot6 \times$ radius of moon.$\Big)$

(5) *Earth satellite.* When a satellite moves in a circle close to the earth's surface, then $mv^2/r = mg$, where $g = 10$ m/s² (approx.). Thus $v^2 = rg$, so $v = \sqrt{rg}$. Hence the period $T$ in the orbit $= 2\pi r/v = 2\pi\sqrt{r/g}$ $= 2\pi\sqrt{(6\cdot4 \times 10^6/10)} = 4900$ seconds approx., since the radius of the earth, $r = 6\cdot4 \times 10^6$ m. The period of the satellite is thus about 81 minutes.